A POCKETFUL OF STEAM PROBLEMS (WITH SOLUTIONS!)

DAN HOLOHAN

For additional copies, contact
HeatingHelp.com
63 North Oakdale Avenue,
Bethpage, NY 11714.
Telephone: 1-800-853-8882
Fax: 888-486-9637
www.HeatingHelp.com

Manufactured in U.S.A.

First Printing, February, 1996
Second Printing, December, 1998
Third Printing, February, 2001
Fourth Printing, February, 2002
Fifth Printing, January, 2004
Sixth Printing, August, 2005
Seventh Printing, October, 2007
Eighth Printing, November, 2009

ISBN 0-9743960-1-X

9 780974 396019

For Alan Levi,

Ace Troubleshooter

As You Begin to Troubleshoot...

1 Forget what you know about hot water systems. Remember that steam is a gas, and that it plays by its own rules.

2 Understand, too, that steam is dynamic. It moves very quickly, and it always wants to condense into water.

3 Think in terms of the system, not just the symptoms. Take it all in.

4 Don't try to solve the problem before you've completely defined it.

5 Remember that with steam, the problem and the cause of the problem are rarely in the same place. Wander around.

6 Always round up the usual suspects: Air, Dirt, and Piping.

7 Go through the possible causes of the problems you'll find in this handbook. And remember, the possible cause you skip just might be the actual one.

WHAT'S YOUR PROBLEM?

Problems that plague
ALL STEAM SYSTEMS

WHAT'S YOUR PROBLEM?

*(Check, too, the following sections
for the type of system you're troubleshooting)*

Problems that plague
ONE-PIPE STEAM SYSTEMS

*(Check, too, the Problems that plague
ALL STEAM SYSTEMS section)*

Problems that plague
TWO-PIPE STEAM SYSTEMS

*(Check, too, the Problems that plague
ALL STEAM SYSTEMS section)*

WHAT'S YOUR PROBLEM?

Problems that plague
MECHANICALLY INDUCED VACUUM SYSTEMS

(Check, too, the Problems that plague
ALL STEAM SYSTEMS section
and the Problems that plague
TWO-PIPE STEAM SYSTEMS section)

Problems that plague
VAPOR and VAPOR/VACUUM SYSTEMS

(Check, too, the Problems that plague
ALL STEAM SYSTEMS section
and the Problems that plague
TWO-PIPE STEAM SYSTEMS section)

WHAT'S YOUR PROBLEM?

Problems that plague
COMMERCIAL STEAM SYSTEMS

WHAT'S YOUR PROBLEM?

(Check, too, the Problems that plague
ALL STEAM SYSTEMS section
and the Problems that plague
TWO-PIPE STEAM SYSTEMS section)

Problems that plague
ALL STEAM SYSTEMS

THE PIPING IS THE WRONG SIZE.

There are too many radiators attached to the pipes.

A steam pipe can carry just about any load if you get the pressure high enough, and if you don't care about velocity noise. The challenge with steam heating, however, is to deliver the right load to the radiators using low pressure, usually not more than 2 psi at the boiler. The Dead Men sized the radiators to heat the space on the coldest day of the year with about 1 psi pressure at the radiator. They used low pressure steam so the radiators wouldn't overheat and the fuel bills wouldn't be too high. They worked with pipe sizing charts that showed them the load limits for steam heating (See *The Golden Rules of Hydronic Heating*). If you connect too much radiation to a steam main or riser you won't be able to heat it all, unless you raise the pressure to an abnormally high level. And when you raise the pressure, you create other problems: high fuel bills, water level problems at the boiler, and noise.

Check the radiation against the carrying capacity of the pipe. Try closing some radiators. If that doesn't help, you may have to repipe.

The steam's not leaving the boiler at the right pressure.

If you size the pipes for a certain pressure, you have to run the system at that pressure. Steam is a compressible gas. The higher you raise the pressure of the steam, the tighter you'll squeeze it. Suppose, for instance, you size your pipes to carry, say, 100-psi steam pressure. If you try to run the system at less than 100-psi

3

pressure, the steam will expand and the velocity through the pipe will increase dramatically. That's because, at the lower pressure, the steam takes up more space. And since it takes up more space, it has to move faster. The increase in velocity will pull water out of the boiler. You'll wind up with water level problems at the boiler, water hammer in the system, and very wet steam at the end of the line. This is why in commercial steam systems the operator will always bring the boiler up to full pressure before opening the valves to the piping.

Check the steam pressure and make sure it's right for your application.

You need to crank the pressure down.

In a steam heating system it pays to run on very low pressure (usually less than 2 psi); this is what the Dead Men intended. Typically, they sized one-pipe steam systems to have a pressure drop of about one ounce per 100 feet of equivalent run. With two-pipe steam, they figured about two ounces per 100 feet. Even in a large building, it doesn't take much pressure to get the steam to the farthest radiator. By cranking the pressure down you'll save fuel and allow the condensate to return more quickly from the system.

When in doubt, crank it down. If it's a space-heating system and it won't heat on low pressure, the system is probably air locked. Deal with the air and crank the pressure down.

It's a commercial steam system, and you're not delivering the right pressure to the heating equipment.

Commercial steam systems and steam heating systems are not the same. With commercial steam, your goal is to make the surface of something really hot. The higher you raise the steam pressure, the hotter that surface will get. When engineers size pipes for commercial steam systems, they have to know how much pressure they'll need at the end of the line (at their process equipment or heat exchanger). They already know how much pressure they'll have at their boiler or pressure reducing valve station. They'll size their pipes to allow for a certain drop in pressure from one end to the other. In doing this, they'll also consider the velocity of the steam. If the steam moves too quickly, it will make noise. It will also erode the pipes.

Check the pressure drop and the velocity of the steam against the pipe size using a Moody Friction Flow chart (available from steam trap manufacturers). Make adjustments, if necessary.

Steam and condensate are flowing in opposite directions.

If they are, the pipes have to be larger. Usually they're one size larger than they would be if the steam and condensate were flowing in the same direction. The pitch also has to be doubled when you have counterflow. On steam mains, the proper pitch for counterflow is one inch in ten feet.

Check the pitch with a line level, and check the pipe size against the connected load.

THERE'S WATER HAMMER IN THE SYSTEM.

The pipes don't have the right pitch.

In any steam system, the condensate is supposed to drain by gravity back to the boiler or the condensate receiver. If water lays in the pipes between firing cycles, steam will pick it up and drive it into the first available fitting. Water hammer from bad pipe pitch usually happens when the system first starts. Steam will also rapidly condense over a puddle of water causing the water to snap violently up into the partial vacuum left by the condensed steam. The proper pitch for parallel flow steam mains is one inch in 20 feet. For counterflow mains, it's one inch in ten feet.

Check the pitch with a line level.

I nch in 10'

The near-boiler piping doesn't meet the manufacturer's specs.

Nowadays, boiler manufacturers consider the near-boiler pip-ing to be a part of the boiler. They use it to help dry the steam before it heads out toward the system. If the near-boiler piping doesn't meet the manufacturer's specs, you could be throwing water up into the piping, and this will cause water hammer.

Get the boiler manufacturer's installation-and-operating manual and check the piping on the job against the drawings in their booklet.

The steam quality is bad.

The quality of the steam greatly affects water hammer. It's not just faulty near-boiler piping that can throw water up into the system. Dirty water or water that has a too-high pH can do it as well. This type of water hammer usually happens during the middle of the firing cycle.

Look closely at the boiler's gauge glass. If the steam is dry, the part of the gauge glass above the water line should be dry as well. Try raising the water line to within an inch of the top of the gauge glass. If the water in the boiler is clean, it will not surge over the top of the gauge glass.

Check the pH of the water with pH paper. A good pH for a steam system ranges between seven and nine. If the pH gets to 11, the water will start to prime and foam and carry over into the system, causing water hammer. Dead Men often added vinegar to steam heating systems to lower the pH and lessen the priming and surging.

Make sure the piping is right, and that the water is clean.

The boiler is overfired.

If you overfire a boiler, the water will surge violently and some water will carry over into the pipes. This type of water hammer usually happens during the middle of the firing cycle. You should fire to the connected load of the boiler (piping and radiation). This is the boiler's D.O.E. Heating Capacity load.

Don't oversize replacement boilers. Always check the firing rate against the connected load.

The steam pipes aren't insulated at all.

You're supposed to insulate the supply pipes in a steam system so the steam doesn't condense on its way to the radiators. Bare pipes lose five times as much heat as insulated pipes. Without insulation, the piping's ability to condense steam may exceed the boiler's ability to produce steam. You'll often wind up with radiators at the ends of the main that won't heat well. But worse than that, you'll wind up with water hammer when the system first starts. The cold, uninsulated pipes create more condensate than they can handle. When the steam hits all that water, you get water hammer.

Insulate the steam lines.

The boiler's water line is priming or surging.

Dirt is usually the culprit here. When you see droplets of water in the part of the gauge glass above the water line, it's time to clean the boiler. If the boiler is priming and surging, it's also probably throwing water up into the piping, and that can cause water hammer.

Try raising the water line to within an inch of the top of the gauge glass. If the water in the boiler is clean, it will not surge over the top of the gauge glass. If it does, clean the boiler and the system piping.

There's a long nipple on the Hartford Loop.

There should be either a close nipple or a wye fitting at the point where the equalizer and the wet return join to form the Hartford Loop. If you use a long nipple between the boiler's equalizer and the wet return, the returning water will surge forward violently as steam bubbles condense in the equalizer. A close nipple or wye fitting will lessen the distance the returning condensate has to travel and cure the water hammer. This type of water hammer usually happens near the end of the firing cycle.

Check this critical point in your gravity-return systems, and make sure it has either a close nipple or a wye fitting.

The Hartford Loop's close nipple or wye fitting is too close to the boiler's water line.

Check to see if the water level in the boiler can drop to a point where steam gains access to the wet return through the boiler's equalizer. If it can, the steam will quickly push down into the wet return and create water hammer. This usually happens toward the end of the cycle.

Check the boiler manufacturer's specifications on the proper level for the close nipple or wye fitting. If it's too high, lower it to the proper level.

The system was flooded.

Steam pipes are supposed to carry air, steam and a little bit of water. If someone left a feed valve open and the pipes filled with water, there's a good chance all the pipes have sagged on their hangers. This is a sure cause of water hammer. You'll hear it when the system first starts.

Flooding also causes sludge to wash down from the radiators. This sludge can lodge in the horizontal runouts to the risers and cause water hammer in the middle of the cycle. It will also make it difficult to deliver steam to the upper radiators.

There's a telltale sign that there's sludge in the riser: The radiator vents will "pant." Remove the vent and hold a lit match next to the hole. Watch the flame. As the radiator "pants," the flame will tilt toward and away from the hole. This happens because steam is quickly condensing in a pocket of trapped water near the base of the riser.

You may have to disconnect the riser and flush the lines to cure this one. Also, make sure you check the pitch of the mains with a line level.

The mains aren't properly dripped.

If enough water hangs around in the mains too long it's bound to run into steam and that's when the water hammer begins. To get rid of the water, you have to drip the mains. In mains where the steam and condensate travel in the same direction, there should be a drip line every 150 feet. If the steam and the condensate flow in opposite directions you need a drip every 50 feet.

If you have a one-pipe steam riser that feeds up more than one floor you should ideally drip it into a wet return or into a dry return through a loop seal or a steam trap. Dripping two-pipe

17

steam risers isn't as critical because the condensate returns through a separate line. Just keep in mind that any steam pipe will be more efficient if you drip it.

To avoid water hammer, always keep the steam and the condensate as far away from each other as you can. Look around for places where water can gather and drip it.

The gravity-return line is clogged.

It's going to happen eventually because a steam heating system is open to the atmosphere. The pipes corrode, and sludge, rust and sediment washes down into the gravity wet-return line where the condensate moves very slowly. As the return line clogs, the condensate has a tough time flowing out of the main and into the wet return. If water lays in the main, it will meet steam, and that's when the hammering begins. This usually happens at the far ends of the mains and almost always in the middle of the firing cycle. Water will also squirt from your end-of-main vents.

You can usually flush the returns to get rid of the sludge, but there will be times when it will be easier to replace those returns. Do one or the other.

The system has motorized valves.

If it's a gravity-return system, and there are motorized valves on the supply lines, water will back out of the boiler when a valve closes against steam pressure. Adding a check valve to the return doesn't help much. Sure, it will keep the water from backing out of the boiler, but the steam pressure in the boiler will quickly overcome the lack of steam pressure downstream of the closed motorized valve. Condensate won't drain from the mains, and water hammer will follow.

Motorized valves really have no business being on a gravity-return system. You may have to add a boiler-feed pump and steam traps to cure this one. Always avoid using motorized valves on gravity-return systems.

The radiators aren't pitched properly.

A one-pipe steam radiator has to pitch back toward its supply valve so the condensate can flow out of the radiator. If you let the condensate build up inside the radiator, you'll have water hammer and squirting radiator air vents. Use a bubble level to check the pitch.

When you're dealing with a large radiator, check the pitch from section to section. Big radiators often sag in the middle, and a long level might not pick this up. Don't go by eye because your eyes can play tricks on you.

Use small blocks of wood or plastic checkers to prop up the end of the radiator. Notice, too, how an old radiator will dig a trench into a wooden floor. That comes from years of expansion and contraction. Don't go by eye when you're checking the pitch. Always use a level.

It's one-pipe steam, and the supply valves aren't fully opened.

If they're not, you'll get water hammer as steam and condensate try to pass each other in that tight space. The valve on a one-pipe steam radiator is a service valve. It has to be either fully opened or fully closed. Anything between will cause water hammer problems. If you think the valve is fully opened and you're still getting water hammer, check to make sure parts of the valve haven't fallen off and lodged in the valve's seat.

If the valve is new, check its internal size. Steam supply valves of the old days had more space inside than their modern replacements. You may have to use a bigger size.

The steam traps aren't working.

A two-pipe steam system is like a ladder. Each radiator is a rung on that ladder, and at the end of each rung you'll find a steam trap. Part of the trap's job is to keep steam from entering the no-pressure side of the "ladder." If even one trap fails in the open position, steam will jump across and hammer into the water that's trying to drain from the other radiators. This water hammer will damage the working steam traps, and that will make the problem even worse.

At the ends of mains and at the base of risers, float & thermostatic and bucket traps serve the same purpose as radiator traps. If they fail in the open position, or, with bucket traps, if they lose their

prime water, steam will move into the dry return line
water hammer. Trap maintenance is essential. Don't

The radiator air vents are too quick.

Quick vents let the air race out of a radiator, but they also let
the steam race in. When you quickly heat a large radiator, you're
going to get a lot of condensate. That heavy load of condensate
can't drain easily against the steam that's rushing through the supply valve. The result is water hammer and a squirting air vent.

If you suspect this is your problem, try an air vent with a
slower venting rate. This simple trick often works wonders when it
comes to water hammer. Not every radiator needs a quick vent.

In replacing the boiler, someone turned a wet return into a dry return.

If you have a gravity-return system the lowest, horizontal, steam-carrying pipe has to be a minimum distance above the boiler. In one-pipe steam, that distance is 28 inches. In two-pipe, gravity-return steam, you need a minimum of 30 inches for every pound of pressure in the boiler. So, for instance, if you operate the boiler at two psi, you need 60 inches. If you operate the boiler at three psi, you need 90 inches. The Dead Men knew this, and they piped their wet and dry returns accordingly. A new boiler with a low water line just might turn a wet return into a dry return. If it does, you'll have some very memorable water hammer in the middle of the firing cycle.

Measure the distance between the boiler's water line and the lowest steam-carrying pipe. And take your time looking around the basement because that pipe could be anywhere.

THE FUEL BILLS ARE ABNORMALLY HIGH.

The air vents aren't working.

And if they're not, the system will trap air and drive the fuel bills up. Steam and air are both gases, but steam is lighter than air so the two won't mix. When the steam heads down a pipe, it pushes air ahead of itself. If the air can't escape from a point near the end of the pipe (through a vent), the steam will just compress it. The pressure will build and the burner will shut off on the pressuretrol. The building will stay cold because the radiators and mains contain air instead of steam. Someone will probably show up and raise the pressure, and that's when you'll start to burn more fuel. The higher pressure compresses the air a bit more, but usu-

25

ally not enough to heat the building. The higher you raise the pressure, the bigger the fuel bills will be.

If you want to save fuel, fix the air vents. Take them off and try to blow through them. If they're clogged, boil them in vinegar for an hour. If they still don't work, replace them.

The burner is short-cycling.

It could be because the air vents aren't working. A short-cycling burner runs very inefficiently, and that leads to greater fuel usage. Check the air vents, and change them if necessary.

Check the firing rate of the burner as well. You should be firing to the boiler's connected load (the piping and radiation) and no more. If your burner is too large it will raise the system pressure very quickly, and then shut off on the pressuretrol.

If you combine an oversized burner with clogged air vents you'll magnify the problem—and you'll increase the fuel bills. If the burner is oversized it will also throw water up into the system. That leads to wet steam, and wet steam can also make the burner short-cycle. The pressure builds quickly as the steam leaves the boiler and confronts the air. But because there's so much water in the steam, the steam quickly condenses, and that makes the burner come on again.

Short-cycling wastes fuel. Find the cause and eliminate it.

The steam traps aren't working.

If the steam traps on the radiators or at the ends of the main fail in the open position, steam will enter the return lines. Once there, it will equalize the pressures on the supply and return sides of the system. When that happens, the flow of steam stops. The people in the building have no heat. Someone raises the pressuretrol settings, and adjusts the thermostat to make the burner run longer. The higher pressure, combined with the longer steaming cycle, will overheat the radiators that were already getting steam. Those people will probably open their windows. The radiators that weren't heating before will get a bit hotter, but at what cost?

When steam traps are not working, fuel bills soar. There is no substitute for steam trap maintenance in a steam-heated building. Find the defective traps and repair or replace them.

You can check thermostatic radiator traps with a thermometer. There should be at least a ten-degree temperature drop from one side to the other. Float & thermostatic and bucket traps have no temperature drop across them. Check these by opening the line downstream of the trap. You should see mostly condensate with some flash steam come from the trap. If you see live steam, repair or replace the trap. Before you replace a bucket trap, make sure it's primed with water. If a bucket trap loses its prime, it will blow live steam.

The burner is undersized.

If the burner is too small, it will run 24 hours a day and not heat the building. It's like putting a pot on simmer. You're putting in enough heat to make the water boil gently, but not enough to deliver steam to the ends of the mains. Remember, the boiler's ability to produce steam has to match the system's ability to condense steam.

Think for a minute about a high/low-fire burner. You begin with the big flame because both the insulated pipes and the radiators are cold. The big flame lets you drive steam out to the ends of the mains. Since the piping represents at least one-third of the total load, you need that big flame on start-up. But once you've made the insulated piping hot, the burner can drop to the low-fire setting because the insulated piping's ability to condense steam has lessened.

Now imagine you start with the little flame instead of the big flame. Can you imagine how difficult it will be to push steam to the farthest radiator? This is why you should never undersize burners. If the burner is too small, the fuel bills will be very high. Always fire to the connected load.

There's a hole in the boiler.

Now, this isn't a hole you can see. It's an internal hole caused by oxygen corrosion. It happens to a cast-iron boiler that takes on a lot of fresh feed water. The oxygen boils out of the water and eats a hole through the metal at the boiler's water line. The water steams off and goes up the flue. You can't see it unless you're look-ing at the chimney. It looks like white smoke, but it's not smoke; it's water vapor. The fuel bills increase because the burner never shuts off on high pressure.

And since a lot of steam goes up the chimney, you wind up with the same effect you'd have if the burner were undersized. It runs on and on, but the farthest radiators never get hot.

To check for a hole, flood the boiler up into the header piping. You'll know you have a problem if you see water pouring out of the boiler's jacket. By the way, if you have an automatic water feeder, it pays to install an inexpensive water meter on the feed line. Keep a log of the meter reading and you'll have an early warning of a system leak or a hole in the boiler.

The device that controls the firing cycle is either defective or in the wrong place.

Larger steam-heated buildings have heat-timing devices. These devices will fill the piping and radiation with steam on a call for heat. Then they'll run the boiler for a certain time, based on the outdoor temperature.

Some control manufacturers use a pressuretrol to figure out when steam fills the piping and radiation. It's easy to trick these pressuretrols. All it takes is a bit of dirt either in the pressuretrol or the pigtail. If the fuel bills are high, check that pressuretrol and pigtail.

Other heat-timing devices use thermistors to sense temperature rather than pressure. Usually, you place the thermistor at the end of the longest steam main, but there are no fixed rules. It varies from building to building. However, if the thermistor is on a main that has a clogged air vent, the burner will run all the time. That's because the trapped air will keep the steam from reaching the thermistor. Check, too, for thermistors that wind up on cold water lines, drain lines and, yes, even gas lines!

If you have a gravity-return system, make sure the thermistor is high enough on the main. It needs to be below the "A" or "B" Dimension so the rising condensate doesn't cover and cool it. (See *The Lost Art of Steam Heating* for a complete discussion of "A" and "B" Dimensions.)

The thermostat is either not working or it's in the wrong place.

A smaller steam system will run off a space thermostat. The thermostat probably will be somewhere in the center of the building, but it might also be in the coldest room. If it is in the coldest room, the other rooms might overheat, and that will make people open their windows. An open window will always mean a higher fuel bill.

Check to make sure you have the thermostat properly calibrated. And use an ammeter when you're checking. Don't guess at that anticipator setting.

If the thermostat has a mercury switch, make sure the thermostat hangs level on the wall. See if cold drafts hit the thermostat, or if it's hanging on a poorly insulated, outside wall. All these things lead to higher-than-normal fuel bills.

The boiler is dirty.

If the boiler is sooty, it's going to burn lots of fuel. Check it out, and give it a good vacuuming if it needs it. If the boiler has a chamber, make sure that chamber hasn't collapsed, either fully or partially. If you're burning oil, check to see if you have the correct nozzle. Check both the firing rate and the flame pattern. If the burner runs on gas, check the gas pressure and clock the meter.

A great investment you can make in any steam system is to install a stack thermometer in the breeching. Keep a log showing the stack temperature. Start the log right after you've cleaned the boiler thoroughly. When you see the temperature rise, you know it's time to clean the boiler again.

THE RADIATORS WON'T HEAT ALL THE WAY ACROSS.

Are you sure they're supposed to?

Keep in mind the Dead Men sized those radiators to heat the room to a comfortable temperature on the coldest day of the year. That's the day during which the radiators should be hot all the way across. If the radiator you're working with isn't hot all the way across, check the room temperature with a good thermometer. If the room is the correct temperature, the burner is probably off. Without the burner there can be no more steam. And without more steam, the radiator can't possibly get any hotter than it already is. If the radiator is grossly oversized for the room, it may *never* get hot all the way across.

If the room is the right temperature, don't worry about how hot the radiator gets.

The room with the partially heated ONE-PIPE steam radiator is too cold.

If it's a one-pipe radiator, check the air vent. If the vent is clogged, the air can't get out and the steam can't get in. Painters do a real job on air vents.

Check the radiator's pitch while you're at it. If the pitch is wrong, there may be a buildup of water in the radiator. That will cause the steam to quickly condense before the radiator can get hot all the way across. If the pitch is wrong, the radiator will also gurgle and rumble and the vent will probably spit.

There may also be a buildup of sludge in the horizontal runout to the radiator's riser. That sludge will trap water, and the water will condense the steam before it reaches the radiator. A "panting" air vent is a good clue that you're having this problem.

Clean the radiator and, if necessary, the riser. And make sure you have the radiator pitched the right way.

The room with the partially heated TWO-PIPE steam radiator is too cold.

If it is, check the steam trap by opening it up. Take care not to get burned. If air rushes out of the trap and the steam races through the radiator, you know either that trap or a nearby trap is defective. Find it, and repair or replace it.

Never add an air vent to a two-pipe steam radiator. The air vent will make the radiator hot, but if the steam traps have failed, the condensate won't drain from the radiator. You'll wind up with water hammer, further steam trap damage, higher-than-normal fuel bills, and severe water level problems in your boiler or boiler-feed pump receiver.

There is no substitution for steam trap maintenance.

THE RETURN LINES ARE CLOGGED.

The system is corroding.

All steam systems are open to the atmosphere. Whenever you mix water with iron and steel you're going to get rust, and that rust is going to wash down into the returns. Eventually, those returns will clog, and the condensate will rise into the steam mains. The symptoms of this problem are water hammer at mid-cycle and water level problems in the boiler.

You should regularly clean and flush the returns.

The system is taking on too much feed water.

Fresh water contains lots of oxygen, and oxygen causes corrosion. Feed water also contains minerals that will settle out when you heat the water. Those minerals (mostly calcium and magnesium) form a rock-hard scale that can quickly clog your return lines.

If you have an automatic feeder and any buried steam or condensate lines, it pays to install an inexpensive water meter on the feed line. Keep a log of how much water enters the system. It's normal for all open steam systems to take on some water, but if you see the meter reading suddenly jump, you know you have a leak. Find it and repair it.

You have to clean the clogged returns.

To do this properly, you'll have to disconnect the returns at both ends and flush them through under pressure. This may be harder to do than it sounds, especially if you don't have anywhere to put the crud you'll be flushing out of those old lines. And even if you can force water through under pressure, you may not be able to clear those old lines. Remember, once you reconnect the return lines, there will be very little pressure available to make the condensate flow back to the boiler.

If you flush returns regularly, they'll be less likely to clog.

The return doesn't have a flush valve.

Chances are you don't have a way to flush those lines without taking them apart. But if you get an opportunity to install a flush valve, it will help you clear the lines the next time around. A flush valve on a steam system is like a purge valve on a hot water heating system. You install a gate valve on the return line, just before it enters the Hartford Loop. Right before the gate valve, install a tee with a full-size, full-port ball valve.

To flush the lines, close the gate valve, and fire the boiler. When you build up some pressure, open the ball valve. The steam will push the crud out of the system. You'll have to feed the boiler while you're doing this, of course, because the condensate won't be returning from the system. This method works especially well when you're trying to clean a new boiler.

All steam systems need to be flushed regularly.

You have to replace the wet return.

If the wet return is clogged beyond salvation, you'll have to replace it. If you're dealing with a buried return line your job is going to be a tough one because you'll probably have to jackhammer the floor. If you put the return back in the same place, wrap it in foam insulation to protect it against the concrete.

You'd like to replace the wet return with a dry return.

Be careful here. There's a reason the Dead Man ran a wet return. On a gravity-return system, there may not be enough height between the end of the main and the boiler water line to allow the condensate to return through a dry return. Or there may be risers dripping down into the wet return from upper floors.

If you use a dry return, steam might have access to those drip lines. It will flow up the riser as condensate tries to fall down. That can cause water hammer. It's possible to run a dry return, but you'll have to use loop seals between the riser drip and the dry return. Go ahead and raise your return line, but connect your riser drips from their present location at the floor into your new dry return. What you'll wind up with will be loop seals. A loop seal is a U-tube that fills with water and keeps the steam from working its way up into the riser drips.

You'd like to use a condensate-transfer pump instead of a wet return.

It may make sense to abandon an old wet return and pick up the condensate with a small condensate-transfer pump. From the pump, you can transfer water back to the boiler through a much smaller line (usually three-quarter inch). You can also run this line overhead if that's more convenient.

You'll need a properly sized F&T trap at the end of the main, just before the condensate-transfer pump. Drain the F&T into the transfer pump, and run your new line back to the boiler room. Ideally, you'll be dumping your condensate into a boiler-feed pump, but it's also feasible to go directly into the boiler from the transfer pump.

THERE'S A BAD ODOR COMING FROM THE SYSTEM.

The one-pipe steam system has an odor.

One reason the Dead Men invented two-pipe steam at the turn of the century was to get rid of the odor that often wafted out of their one-pipe steam systems. Since a steam system is open to the atmosphere, it fills with air every time the steam condenses. When the steam comes back up, it pushes the air out the air vents and into the rooms. As the system corrodes, you'll sometimes get an odor with the vented air. It just might smell musty, like steam. Or it might smell worse.

Clean the system with trisodium phosphate to get rid of the odor.

46

There are chemicals in the boiler.

What sort of chemicals are they? If you use too much of a good thing, you're liable to get a bad odor in the rooms. Some people add vinegar to steam systems to reduce the pH of the water and cure priming and surging. If the odor in the room smells like vinegar, it just might be vinegar! Check the chemicals you're using and adjust the dosage.

Someone recently worked on the boiler.

You may be smelling pipe dope or flux. There also may be dirt in the boiler, and if that dirt is organic, it will break down and form gasses that are rough on the nose.

47

Clean the boiler and the system piping with trisodium phosphate.

There's a lot of feed water entering the boiler.

Feed water contains minerals and dissolved solids that can give an odor when boiled. If there's an automatic water feeder on the boiler, close it for an hour and see if the boiler shuts itself off on low water.

If it's a larger system, install an inexpensive water meter on the feed line, and keep track of how much water enters the system.

It's intentional.

I remember this posh apartment building in New York City that suffered from an odor of urine. Turns out it was urine! The superintendent, unhappy with his holiday tips, decided to save his urine in a big coffee can. Each evening, before going off duty, he removed the boiler's relief valve and poured his savings into the boiler. The odor wafted up into the one-pipe steam radiators of the filthy rich. Why did the superintendent do this? Because he could.

THE SYSTEM IS LOSING WATER.

You can't see all the pipes.

If you can't see them, suspect them. This is especially true of buried lines. Condensate contains a mild solution of carbonic acid that can eat through steel. If you're not venting the system properly, the level of carbonic acid will be higher than normal. If a pipe is buried in concrete, the concrete can be aggressive enough to put holes in the pipe.

If you can't see the pipes, suspect them. If they're very old, replace them.

The main vents or radiator vents are losing water or steam.

You can lose a lot of water through an air vent. In apartment buildings, tenants sometimes remove the air vents from a radiator or two. They like what the hole left by the missing vent does for the humidity level in their apartments during the winter. Remember, though, what you lose through the vents you have to make up at the boiler.

If the system isn't well vented, the velocity of the escaping air will increase through whatever vents are working. High-velocity air carries dirt toward the good vents and clogs them. If the vent can't close tightly because there's dirt in its seat, lots of steam will escape. You'll have make up that missing water at the boiler.

Make sure all your vents are working properly.

The system suffers from water hammer.

Water hammer is so destructive it can actually pull pipes out of fittings. It can also destroy air vents and steam traps. Water hammer blasts open holes through which water will flow to the outside. And then you have to make up that water back at the boiler.

Get to the source of the water hammer and get rid of it.

There's a hole in the boiler.

Now this isn't a hole you can see. It's an internal hole cause by oxygen corrosion. It happens to cast-iron boilers when they take on a lot of fresh feed water. The oxygen boils out of the water and eats a hole through the metal right at the boiler's water line. The water steams off and goes up the flue.

You can't see it unless you're looking at the chimney. It looks like white smoke, but it's not smoke; it's water vapor. To check for a hole, flood the boiler up into the header piping. You'll know you have a problem if you see water pouring out of the boiler's jacket.

Check under the jacket for cracks in the boiler that may not be large enough to cause a flood on the floor. The water may be evaporating on the hot cast iron. Is it unusually humid in the boiler room? If it is, there may be a crack in the boiler. Check it out.

And by the way, if the boiler is leaking, don't' try to fix it with dope. That stuff may stop the leak, but it will also contaminate the water to a point where the boiler will produce nothing but wet steam. You can't heat a building with wet steam.

The near-boiler piping is all copper.

Copper headers come apart when the expansion caused by the

hot steam starts twisting them. This is especially true if the boiler has two or more risers to the header. As the soldered fittings let go, the steam begins to leak—and you can lose a lot of water through a leaky soldered joint.

Be smart and pipe your steam boilers with threaded steel instead of copper.

THE SYSTEM TAKES A LONG TIME TO HEAT.

The system doesn't have main vents.

Steam will always follow the path of least resistance. Since it's a gas, it doesn't understand the difference between up and down. All it knows is OUT! Steam will always head for the air vents.

If you don't have any main vents, the steam will compress the trapped air and stop moving. If you have main vents, steam will travel quickly through the mains and reach the radiators in no time at all.

Main vents belong near the ends of the mains, but never put them in a tee right at the very end of the main. If you do, water hammer might clobber them within the first few cycles. Pipe your

55

main vents at least 15 inches back from the end of the main, and six to ten inches up on a nipple. This means you may have to cut and thread the pipe in place to get the main vents in, but it's well worth the effort.

Don't install a three-quarter-inch vent in a one-eighth-inch hole you drilled and tapped in the main. You can't vent much air through a hole that small.

You hear air hissing from the air vents.

In a properly vented steam system, you won't notice the air venting. Think about it. The fact that you can hear the vents hiss means the air doesn't have enough ways out. The hissing is the sound of high-velocity air trying to get out. Why is the air moving at high velocity? Because you don't have enough vents.

High-velocity air can carry sediment toward the working vents and clog them. So when you hear the vents hissing, they're trying

Vents are missing

to tell you something. Add main vents (or *more* main vents) to the system.

add more vents

The boiler is making wet steam.

Check the near-boiler piping against the manufacturer's specifications. If the piping can't separate the water from the steam, the water will condense the steam, and it will take a long time to heat the building.

Check, too, the water's cleanliness and pH. You may have to clean the boiler and the system, and balance the water's pH with chemicals to get it right. A good pH for a steam boiler ranges between seven (neutral) and nine (mildly alkaline).

The burner isn't firing to the connected load.

The burner's ability to produce steam has to match the system's ability to condense steam. Your firing rate must match the piping and radiation load. If it doesn't, it will take a long time to heat the building.

A flame that's too small is the equivalent of trying to melt an iceberg by spraying warm water on it from a garden hose. Check that flame against the connected load and adjust it, if necessary.

The steam pressure is too high.

Check the cut-in setting on the pressuretrol. High pressure can shut air vents and keep them closed. You'll be pushing steam at trapped air, and the building will stay cold because the air can't get out. If you set your pressuretrol's cut-in setting at ½ psi you'll never have a problem.

The pressuretrol's cut-out setting is another thing. It should be no higher than the pressure it takes to get steam from the boiler to the farthest radiator. The pressure you need is a function of pipe size and boiler size, and the Dead Men figured it out years before you and I were born.

When in doubt, crank the pressure down.

There's a water leg before the condensate- or boiler-feed pump receiver.

In two-pipe systems, you have steam traps on the radiators instead of air vents. The steam pushes the air through the traps, into the dry return and toward the condensate- or boiler-feed pump receiver. The receiver has an atmospheric vent, and that's where the air is heading.

If your return line drops below the inlet to the receiver, however, you'll have problems. That return line isn't under pressure because it's downstream of the radiator and end-of-main F&T traps. As condensate drains from the radiators and pipes, it will pool in that water leg and form a seal. Air won't vent through that water seal, and it will take forever to heat the building.

If the traps are defective they'll mask this problem because there will be enough pressure to force the condensate out of the water leg. A lot of water hammer usually accompanies this evacuation of the water. The noise usually encourages the building owner to have his traps fixed. But once the traps are fixed, he'll have little or no heat because the air can't vent through the water seal. At this point, you have two choices. Raise the return line to eliminate the water seal, or install main vents at the outlet sides of the end-of-main F&T traps.

YOU CAN'T RAISE STEAM PRESSURE ON THE GAUGE.

You're looking for more pressure than you need.

It doesn't take much pressure to heat a building. The Dead Men sized their pipes so that the steam would create a very slight pressure drop from the boiler to the farthest radiator. They worked with charts that measured that pressure drop in ounces per hundred feet of travel. Even in a very large building, the total system pressure drop might be as low as 1 psi. Your boiler gauge might not be accurate enough to measure such a low pressure.

You're not using the right gauge.

The gauges that come with modern steam boilers have a tough time sensing steam when it's at a very low pressure. If you're heating the building, but you're not seeing pressure on the gauge, don't be concerned. If you want to see pressure, install a sensitive, diaphragm-type pressure gauge. Find one with a range of, say, zero to five psi. Then you'll see the needle move.

The air vents pant.

If an air vent alternately blows and sucks air, there's probably too much condensate in the mains. The rapid formation and condensing of steam can cause the panting action. If the steam is condensing that quickly, it's going to find it difficult to make it to the ends of the main. It will take forever for you to heat the building.

Look for things that can make steam condense quickly. There could be missing pipe insulation, wet steam, lack of drips along the main, or an accumulation of sludge in the horizontal runouts to the risers. Look for these things and take care of them.

The burner isn't firing to the connected load.

The burner's firing rate has to match the system's ability to condense steam. In other words, it has to match the piping and radiation load. If your air vents are working, you'll never build pressure because there won't be enough steam to reach them.

Consider this. The only way you can build pressure at the boiler is to fill the system with a gas (steam or air) and then add some more. If the burner is undersized, you'll never fill the system with steam. And if the vents are working, you'll never contain or pressurize the air.

So if you're not seeing pressure, and you're not heating the building, suspect the size of your fire and correct it.

The boiler is making wet steam.

Check the near-boiler piping against the manufacturer's specifications. If the piping can't separate the water from the steam, the water will condense the steam, and your boiler will never build pressure. With this problem, you won't be able to heat the building either.

So if you have no pressure and no heat, check the piping, the water's cleanliness and its pH. You may have to clean the boiler and the system and balance the pH with chemicals.

There's a hole in the boiler.

This happens to cast-iron boilers when they take on a lot of fresh feed water. The oxygen boils out of the water and eats a hole through the metal right at the boiler's water line. The water steams off and goes up the flue. You can't see it unless you're looking at the chimney. It looks like white smoke, but it's not smoke; it's water vapor.

To check for a hole, flood the boiler up into the header piping. You'll know you have a problem if you see water pouring out of the boiler's jacket. If there's a hole in the boiler, you'll never build pressure; and you may not be able to heat the farthest radiators either.

You'll have to replace the damaged boiler sections to fix this one.

THE WATER LINE IS BOUNCING UP AND DOWN IN THE GAUGE GLASS.

The boiler is priming or foaming.

Priming is the violent bouncing of the water. Foaming happens when bubbles form on the surface of the water. Foaming follows priming, and while priming is bad, foaming is worse.

Foaming throws water up into the system and creates water hammer, uneven heating and water level problems within the boiler. If you take a sample of the boiler water and boil it on a stove you'll be able to see if it's foaming. Use a narrow pot when you do this test.

If you see foaming, check the pH of the water. Ideally, the pH should be between seven and nine. High pH (high alkaline) causes foaming and is one of the most common causes of boiler problems.

If the boiler is just surging, it's probably because the water is dirty. Clean the system according to the boiler manufacturer's recommendations.

There's oil in the boiler.

It's very hard to see oil if you're looking in the gauge glass, but it will create a film that causes priming and, in some cases, foaming.

Boiler manufacturers use oil when they thread the boiler's tappings. You use oil when you thread your near-boiler piping. You have to get rid of the oil if you want the new boiler to work well.

Read the manufacturer's instructions on boiler cleaning and follow them until the water stops surging.

There's dirt in the boiler.

When the water is clean, steam bubbles have no problem rising to the surface and breaking free. But when the water is dirty, steam finds it more difficult to escape the water.

As the steam bubbles rise to the surface, they increase in volume. These larger bubbles cause the water line to bounce as they try to break the surface of the dirty water.

Read the manufacturer's instructions on boiler cleaning and follow them until the problem goes away.

The flame is impinging on the metal.

This is a common problem with oil burners and power gas burners. The flame has to be the right size and shape for the chamber. If it's not, it will overheat a part of the boiler and cause steam to form more quickly at that point. As the bubbles of steam race up one side of the boiler, the water on the other side of the boiler will drop to compensate. You'll see this surging action in the gauge glass.

Check the firing rate and flame pattern and correct it if necessary. You may have to add chamber material to solve this problem.

The boiler has very narrow sections.

This is a problem you'll sometimes run into with residential steam boilers. If the sections are too narrow, the rising steam bubbles will lift the boiler water level to a point higher than the level in the gauge glass. This happens because there isn't any steam in the water that's in the gauge glass. The two columns of water (in the boiler and in the gauge glass) sit at different levels until the burner shuts off on pressuretrol's cut-out setting.

When the steam bubbles condense, the water in the boiler falls to a point lower than the water in the gauge glass. The water in the gauge glass offsets this by falling into the boiler. This usually turns on the low-water cutoff or the automatic water feeder. You wind up with nagging water level problems in the boiler.

This type of problem is built into the boiler design, and it's tremendously aggravated by dirt. You can sometimes cure it by underfiring the boiler. That produces fewer steam bubbles so each has more room. But don't underfire to a point where you'll only be simmering the water. And make sure the boiler is as clean as possible.

There are chemicals in the water.

What sort of chemicals are they and how much is in there? Too much can cause the water's pH to rise, and that will make the water foam. Check the pH, and lower it if necessary.

The steam is leaving the boiler too quickly.

This is something you won't see, but it's very important nevertheless. If you undersize your pipes as they leave the boiler, the steam will move faster than it should. The high-velocity steam will pull water with it and that leads not only to surging, but also to water hammer, uneven heating, higher-than-normal fuel bills, and water level problems within the boiler.

Follow the boiler manufacturer's piping directions if you want to stay out of trouble.

The low-water cutoff needs a surge column.

Do you know about surge columns? It's a Dead Man's piping trick. A surge column can lessen the surging in the gauge glass and the low-water cutoff.

A surge column looks just like a gauge glass, except it's made of pipe, not glass. You build it from two tees, a few nipples, and a short length of steel pipe, which you'll place between the bulls of the two tees. Hook up your low-water cutoff to the runs of the two tees.

The surge column takes up most of the surging, leaving you with a more stable water line in the low-water cutoff and the gauge glass. A surge column doesn't solve the surging problem, but it can keep the low-water cutoff from bouncing up and down (and on and off) so much.

THERE'S NO HEAT IN CERTAIN AREAS OF THE BUILDING.

The air can't get out.

Follow the pipes from the boiler to the problem area. If you don't see any air vents, the system is probably air-blocked. Look for a union or a strainer you can easily open. If a rush of air comes out and steam follows, you've found the cause of the problem.

Add air vents.

The boiler is making wet steam.

Check the near-boiler piping against the manufacturer's specifications. If the piping is wrong, the boiler will make wet steam, and you probably won't be able to heat certain parts of the building.

Besides the piping, check the water's cleanliness and its pH. You may have to clean the boiler and the system, and balance the pH with chemicals before you can get that troublesome area hot.

The condensate is draining into the steam mains or header.

The condensate in a one-pipe steam system drains into the main at a 45° angle. The idea is to let the condensate cling to the side of the pipe as it flows into the main. If a one-pipe riser left the top of a main at a 90° angle, the returning condensate would splash down into the onrushing steam and stop it dead in its tracks.

The same reasoning applies to boiler headers. Let's say you have two takeoffs from your header. One is a counterflow main. That means the condensate is going to drain into the header, against the flow of steam.

The other takeoff is a parallel flow line. In this main, the condensate will travel with the steam to the end, and then flow back to the boiler through a wet return.

If your parallel-flow takeoff is the first off the header, you won't have a problem. But if your counterflow takeoff comes first, it's going to drain condensate into the header—right in the way of the steam that's trying to make it to the parallel-flow takeoff. You'll have less heat than you need in that part of the building.

Reverse the order of the takeoffs from the header and you'll solve your problem.

There are too many radiators attached to the mains.

If you don't care about velocity noise, a steam pipe can carry just about any load as long as you get the pressure high enough. The challenge with steam heating, however, is to deliver the right load to the radiators using low-pressure steam (usually not more than 2 psi at the boiler).

The Dead Men sized the radiators to heat the space on the coldest day of the year with about 1 psi pressure at the radiator. They used low-pressure steam so the radiators wouldn't overheat and the fuel bills wouldn't skyrocket. They worked with pipe-sizing charts that showed them the load limits for steam heating (see *The Golden Rules of Hydronic Heating*).

If you connect too much radiation to a steam main or riser you won't be able to heat it all unless you raise the pressure to an abnormally high level. And when you raise the pressure, you create other problems: high fuel bills, water level problems within the boiler and noise.

Check the radiation against the carrying capacity of the pipe. Try shutting off a few radiators. If this doesn't work, you may have to repipe.

The pipes aren't pitched properly.

You need one inch in 20 feet for parallel flow, and one inch in ten feet for counterflow. If you let water hang around, you'll get water hammer, and you'll also get uneven heating because the steam will condense in the water.

Check the pitch with a line level.

The steam pipes aren't insulated at all.

Bare steam pipes have five times the heat loss of insulated steam pipes. If the steam condenses in the basement, it won't be around to condense in the radiators upstairs.

All steam mains must be insulated.

The steam traps aren't working.

If the traps on the radiators or at the ends of the main fail in the open position, steam will enter the return lines. Once there, it will equalize the pressures on the supply and return sides of the system and stop, or severely slow, the movement of steam. You'll wind up with no-heat complaints in certain areas of the building.

If the steam traps fail in the closed position, air won't be able to get out of the radiators, and those radiators will remain ice cold.

There is no substitute for steam trap maintenance in a steam-heated building.

There's not enough steam pressure.

It doesn't take much, but you do need enough pressure to over-come the pressure drop the steam experiences as it moves from the boiler to the farthest radiator. If the Dead Man sized the system for 4 psi and you run it at 3 psi, you'll have problems heating certain areas.

If you suspect this might be the problem, raise the pressure in ½ psi increments and see what happens. But be careful because an air-blocked system can give you the same symptoms.

There's a water leg before the condensate- or boiler-feed pump receiver.

In two-pipe systems, you have steam traps on the radiators instead of air vents. The steam pushes the air through the trap, into the dry return and toward the condensate- or boiler-feed pump receiver. The receiver is vented to the atmosphere, and that's where the air is heading.

If your return line drops below the inlet to the receiver, you'll have problems. That line isn't under pressure because it's downstream of the radiator and end-of-main F&T traps. As condensate drains from the radiators and pipes, it will pool in that water leg and form a seal. Air can't vent through that water seal, so the building will take a long time to heat. Certain areas may never heat!

If the traps are defective, they'll mask this problem because there will be enough pressure to force the condensate out of the

81

water leg. A lot of water hammer usually accompanies this evacuation of the water. The noise encourages the building owner to have his traps fixed. Once he does that, he'll have no heat because the air can't get out. At this point, you have two choices. Raise the return line to eliminate the water seal, or install main vents at the outlet side of the end-of-main F&T traps.

The radiators aren't the right size for the space they serve.

Most steam radiators are too big, but there are some that are undersized. If the radiators are hot and the space is cold, check the size of the radiator against the heat loss of the space.

Also, look for excessive infiltration. A drafty window can cause many comfort-related complaints that have little to do with the steam system.

The radiators or the radiator valves are clogged.

Can steam get into those radiators? Have the valves deterio-rated and fallen apart on the inside? Has enough corrosion gath-ered at the bottom of the radiator to trap water and condense the steam as it tries to enter? It pays to check it out.

Also, if the radiator is in a cabinet, can the air reach through to the hot surfaces? Think like air. Could you get through? If not, clean the cabinet.

THE BOILER IS FLOODED.

The boiler's water line is surging.

Dirty water, a too-high pH, overfiring and improper near-boiler piping can all cause the boiler's water line to surge up and down. If there's an automatic water feeder on the boiler, it will open and close each time the water line rocks. Before long, you'll have a flooded boiler.

Don't blame the automatic water feeder; solve the surging problem by cleaning the boiler, adjusting the firing rate or correcting the improper near-boiler piping.

The boiler has a leaky tankless coil.

Even a tiny pinhole in a tankless coil will flood a boiler because the pressure inside the coil is so much greater than the pressure in the boiler. Isolate the coil and watch the gauge glass for an hour or so. If the coil is the culprit, change it.

The gravity-return system has motorized valves.

To get the water back into the boiler, a gravity-return system has to balance itself like a scale. The "leftover" steam pressure at the end of the main combines with the static weight of the condensate that stacks in the vertical space between the boiler water line and the lowest, horizontal steam-carrying pipe (the "A" or "B"

85

Dimension—see *The Lost Art of Steam Heating*). These two forces overcome the pressure inside the boiler and allow the condensate to enter.

When motorized valves close, you lose that "leftover" pressure at the ends of the mains. The static weight of the returning condensate alone usually isn't enough to overcome the pressure in the boiler, so the water backs out of the boiler. If there's an automatic water feeder, it will open and add water to the boiler. The next time the motorized valve opens, the condensate will flow into the boiler and flood it.

If you use motorized zone valves with a gravity-return system you also must use a boiler-feed pump and end-of-main steam traps.

The boiler has very narrow sections.

This is a problem you'll sometimes run into with residential steam boilers. If the sections are too narrow, the rising steam bubbles will lift the boiler water level to a point higher than the level in the gauge glass. This happens because there isn't any steam in the water in the gauge glass. The two columns of water (in the boiler and in the gauge glass) ride at different levels until the burner shuts off on high pressure.

When the steam bubbles condense, the water in the boiler will fall to a point lower than the water in the gauge glass. The water in the gauge glass offsets this by falling into the boiler. If you have an automatic water feeder, it will open and eventually flood the boiler.

This type of problem is built into the boiler design, and it's tremendously aggravated by dirt. You can sometimes cure it by underfiring the boiler. Underfiring produces fewer steam bubbles, giving each more room. But don't underfire to a point where you'll only be simmering the water. Also, make sure the boiler is as clean as possible.

The water's pH is too high.

It should be between seven and nine. A pH of 11 or higher will make the boiler water foam. Foaming water will leave the boiler with the steam, and that will lower the boiler's water line. The automatic water feeder will respond by adding water to the boiler. When the condensate returns from the system, the boiler will flood.

Correct the pH with chemicals. Ideally, it should range between seven (neutral) and nine (mildly alkaline).

The automatic water feeder isn't closing tightly.

All it takes is a buildup of sediment on the feeder's seat to keep the feeder from closing tightly. Since the pressure in the city water main is so much higher than the pressure in the boiler, water will continue to flow into the boiler and flood it if the feeder isn't tightly closed.

Check the feeder by doing a broken-union test. Bring the boiler water level to the "feeder closed" point. Open a union on the outlet side of the feeder, below the boiler water line. There should be a gate valve or a ball valve after the union to keep water from flowing from the boiler. If the feeder is tightly closed, no water should flow from the union.

If you supply the feeder with hot water, lime scale will accumulate on the feeder's seat and eventually cause the feeder to fail. Feeder manufacturers recommend you feed only with cold water if you want to avoid this problem.

The line between the feeder
and the boiler is clogged.

Some automatic water feeders have a mechanical, float-operated valve. If there's backpressure in the feeder's discharge line, the feeder might not close tightly. Backpressure comes from a buildup of lime scale in the feed line. The feeder stays open and allows water to enter the boiler.

You can check this by doing a broken-union test. Bring the boiler water level to the "feeder closed" point. Open a union on the outlet side of the feeder. Now open the gate valve or ball valve between the union and the boiler. If the line is clear, you should get a steady flow of water from the boiler. If all you get is a trickle, change the line.

The feeder bypass line is leaking.

Check the valve in the feeder bypass line. If it's not holding tightly, water will enter the boiler and flood it. Use a broken-union test to test the valve. Install a union after the bypass gate valve or ball valve, and open it. If your gate valve or ball valve holds, no water should flow from the union. If water does flow through, repair or replace the valve.

There's a check valve in the gravity-return line.

Equalizers make check valves unnecessary, but you'll still find them on many steam systems. If a check valve gets clogged with dirt, it will slow the rate at which condensate returns to the boiler.

If there's an automatic water feeder on the boiler, it will add water. When enough condensate backs up behind the clogged check valve, the valve might open and allow the water back into the boiler. Since the automatic water feeder already replaced that "missing" water, the boiler will flood.

Clean the check valve, or remove its flapper. If the gravity-return system has an equalizer, you don't need a check valve.

The boiler is overfired.

If you overfire a boiler the water will surge violently and some water will carry over into the pipes. An automatic water feeder will replace that water, and the boiler will flood at the end of the steaming cycle. You should fire to the connected load of the boiler (piping and radiation). This is the boiler's D.O.E. Heating Capacity load. Don't oversize replacement boilers.

The near-boiler piping doesn't meet the manufacturer's specs.

Manufacturers know that if the steam leaves the boiler too quickly it will carry water with it. They also know that high-velocity steam can tilt the boiler's water line, and cause a low-water cutoff to operate (or not operate!). That tilting water line can also open an automatic water feeder and flood the boiler. This is why manufacturers tap modern steam boilers with multiple outlets.

The steam boilers of yesteryear were different from the ones we're using today. One outlet may have been enough in the old days because the boiler was much larger and had wider sections and a more generous steam chest. A boiler of the same rating nowadays, however, may need two or three outlets to dry the steam and balance the water line.

This is why it's so important to read the manufacturer's installation instructions and follow them. If you pipe the new boiler the same way as the Dead Man piped the old boiler, you're probably going to get into trouble. Read the boiler manufacturer's instructions thoroughly, and follow them to the letter.

The automatic water feeder is set at the wrong level.

A feeder's job is to maintain a safe, minimum water line, not an operating water level. Don't think of a feeder as a convenience item; it's a backup safety device for the low-water cutoff. If you raise the feed level to the center of the gauge glass the feeder will let water into the boiler before the condensate has a chance to return from the system. When the condensate finally does return from the system, the boiler will flood. Check the manufacturer's installation diagram and, if necessary, make the correction.

Someone is overfeeding the boiler.

Ask around. There may be an enthusiastic superintendent or home owner who likes to feed the boiler while it's steaming. If they add water by hand before the condensate returns, the boiler will flood when the condensate finally does return.

Educate the building owner on the right way to feed a steam boiler. Don't add water by hand unless the boiler is off and the condensate has returned from the system.

THE BURNER SHUTS OFF ON LOW WATER.

The system is leaking.

Do you have buried return lines? If so, they may be leaking.

Are your air vents in good condition? You can lose plenty of water through a leaky air vent.

Are all the valve stems holding tight? A bad packing gland can waste as much steam as a bad air vent.

How about the boiler? Is it in good shape? When you look into the chamber, do you see any rusty areas? Do you see any discolored areas on the burners? The boiler may be leaking.

There may also be a hole in the boiler at its water line. Raise the water level into the header and see if water pours out of the boiler. If it does, you'll have to replace the damaged sections.

The boiler water pH is too high.

The pH should be between seven and nine. A pH of 11 or higher will make the boiler water foam. Foaming water will leave the boiler with the steam. That lowers the boiler's water line and causes nuisance low-water problems.

If there's an automatic water feeder, it will add water to the system. When the condensate returns from the system, the boiler will flood. Correct the pH with chemicals. Ideally, it should range between seven (neutral) and nine (mildly alkaline).

The boiler's water line is priming or surging.

Dirt is usually the culprit here. When you see droplets of water in the part of the gauge glass above the water line, it's time to clean the boiler. If the boiler is priming and surging, it's also probably throwing water up into the piping, and that can make the burner trip out on low water. Try raising the water line to within an inch of the top of the gauge glass. If the water in the boiler is clean, it will not surge over the top of the gauge glass. If it does, clean the boiler with trisodium phosphate.

The near-boiler piping doesn't meet the manufacturer's specs.

Nowadays, boiler manufacturers consider the near-boiler piping to be a part of the boiler. They use it to help dry the steam before it heads out toward the system. If the near-boiler piping doesn't meet the manufacturer's specs, you could be throwing water up into the piping, and this will make the burner shut off on low water.

Check the manufacturer's installation-and-operating manual and make the corrections.

The boiler has very narrow sections.

This is a problem you'll sometimes run into with residential steam boilers. If the sections are too narrow, the rising steam bubbles will lift the boiler water level to a point higher than the level in the gauge glass. This happens because there isn't any steam in the water in the gauge glass. The two columns of water (in the boiler and in the gauge glass) ride at different levels until the burner shuts off on high pressure.

When the steam bubbles condense, the water in the boiler will fall to a point lower than the water in the gauge glass. The water in the gauge glass offsets this by falling into the boiler. The low-water cutoff will shut off the burner. If you have an automatic water feeder, it will open and eventually flood the boiler.

This type of problem is built into the boiler design, and it's tremendously aggravated by dirt. You can sometimes cure it by underfiring the boiler. That produces fewer steam bubbles so each has more room. But don't underfire to a point where you'll only be simmering the water. Also, make sure the water is as clean as possible.

The boiler doesn't contain enough water.

It really doesn't matter how much water the boiler contains. What's important is the amount between the center of the gauge glass and the low-water cutoff point. This is a boiler's operating range.

All boilers lose water to steam at a constant rate of ½ gpm per 240,000 BTU/Hr. (D.O.E. Heating Capacity rating). To keep the boiler from shutting off on low water, the condensate must return before all the water in the operating range turns to steam.

Suppose, for instance, you have a boiler rated at 240,000 BTU/Hr. Let's say it contains five gallons of water in its operating range. Since it loses steam at the rate of ½ gallon per minute, you'll reach the low-water cutoff point in ten minutes. In this example, the condensate must return to the boiler within ten minutes to keep the burner from shutting off on low water. If the condensate takes longer than that to return, you should use a boiler-feed pump.

Keep in mind, too, that things such as clogged returns, bad steam traps, overfiring, dirty water and poor near-boiler piping can create the same problem. Look into these possible causes before you install a boiler-feed pump.

The boiler is being used for both process and space heating.

If it is, you may not have the right combination of controls. A process boiler often loses much of its water to a drain. If you're using a combination feeder/low-water cutoff, the feeder may not keep up with the process boiler's needs. Since the water level drops so quickly, the low-water cutoff will shut off the burner.

When you use a boiler for process only or for both process and space heating, make sure you use a separate low-water cutoff and a separate automatic water feeder. Set the feeder at a level somewhat higher than the level you'd choose for a space heating system where all the condensate returns to the boiler.

THE BOILER WATER IS VERY DIRTY.

You may be asking for too much.

Since a steam system is open to the atmosphere and constantly rusting and corroding, it's very difficult to keep the water pure. You should always expect some discoloration of the water. The problems begin when the water gets dirty enough to cause priming and foaming. That's when you should follow the boiler manufacturer's cleaning instructions.

The installer didn't clean the boiler.

Boiler manufacturers use a lot of oil when they drill and tap the boiler. The installer also uses oil when he threads his pipes. If you don't get rid of that oil, the boiler water might not only appear dirty, it will also prime and foam.

Here's another thing to consider. New boilers act like scouring pads on old steam systems. The dry steam will reach out into the system farther and faster, and dislodge years of dirt and corrosion. When that grime washes back to the boiler, the water will appear very dirty. You may have to clean a replacement steam boiler more than once. Follow the manufacturer's directions.

The buried returns are leaking.

The condensate flowing out of a leaking buried return will create mud. The flow of condensate can carry some of that mud back to the boiler where it shows up as filthy water in the gauge glass. If you've cleaned the system repeatedly and still wind up with dirty water, suspect those buried wet returns.

And even if the water isn't dirty, suspect them anyway. Buried wet returns are always worthy of suspicion.

The system is taking on too much feed water.

Fresh water contains lots of oxygen, and oxygen causes corrosion, which shows up as rusty water. Feed water also contains minerals that will settle out when you heat the water. Those minerals (mostly calcium and magnesium) form a rock-hard scale that can quickly clog your return lines. That forces water up into the returns where it meets steam and creates water hammer. The water hammer can dislodge even more corrosion, which eventually washes down to the boiler and discolors the water. When these things begin to happen, dirty water is usually the least of your problems. Find the source of the excess feed water and get rid of it.

# THE PITCH OF THE PIPES IS WRONG.

Steam and condensate flow in the same direction, and the pitch is less than one inch in 20 feet.

There should be no areas where condensate can gather when the system shuts down. If you let condensate lay between cycles, steam will pick it up on the following cycle and create water hammer.

Check the mains with a line level. Don't trust your eyes.

Steam and condensate flow in opposite directions, and the pitch is less than one inch in ten feet.

Don't let condensate hang around during firing cycles. Make sure it can drain quickly back to the boiler or condensate receiver.

Notice how the pitch of counterflow pipes is twice what it is on parallel flow pipes. This is a very important consideration in steam heating. The condensate and the steam have to be able to get out of each other's way.

Don't trust your eyes; use a line level.

Horizontal runouts to risers feed a second (or higher) floor, and the pitch isn't right.

In a one-pipe steam system, the condensate and the steam have to pass each other in that horizontal runout to the riser. If the riser feeds a radiator on the first floor, the pitch is not so critical because there's usually not that much condensate flowing back. However, when the riser feeds an upper floor (and you can't drip it) you have the additional burden of the piping to consider. A lot of condensate is going to be fighting that steam on its way to the radiator. To avoid water hammer and uneven heating, you should give that runout to the riser a pitch of at least one inch per foot. Use a line level to check it.

The risers aren't dripped.

If you have a one-pipe steam riser that feeds up more than one floor you should, ideally, drip it into a wet return or into a dry return through a loop seal or a steam trap.

Dripping two-pipe steam risers isn't as critical because the condensate returns through a separate line. Just keep in mind that any steam pipe will be more efficient if you drip it. To avoid water hammer, always keep the steam and the condensate as far away from each other as you can.

The mains aren't properly dripped.

Even if the pitch is good, you can still get water hammer if you don't drip those mains. In mains where the steam and condensate travel in the same direction, there should be a drip line every 150 feet. If the steam and the condensate flow in opposite directions, you need a drip line every 50 feet.

If you drip into a gravity wet return, you don't need steam traps. If you drip into a dry return, or a return that ends in a condensate- or boiler-feed pump, use steam traps.

THE BURNER SHORT-CYCLES.

The thermostat is out of calibration.

If it is, the burner will be bouncing on and off. Make sure you use an ammeter when you're checking the calibration. Don't guess at that anticipator's setting.

Check, too, to see if the thermostat has a mercury switch. If it does, make sure the thermostat hangs level on the wall. And check to see if the thermostat is in a cold draft, or if it's hanging on a poorly insulated, outside wall. Make the necessary corrections.

113

The boiler is oversized.

You're supposed to size the boiler and fire the burner to the connected piping-and-radiation load. In the boiler manufacturer's literature, they call this load the D.O.E. Heating Capacity. If your boiler is too big, its ability to produce steam will exceed the system's ability to condense steam. The burner will short-cycle.

You may be able to solve the problem by downfiring the burner, but be careful when you try this. You may downfire to a point where the flue gases begin to condense. Fire only to the connected load.

The boiler is properly sized, but overfired.

If there's too much fire, you'll get lots of steam in a hurry. That will quickly raise the boiler pressure and short-cycle the burner off the pressuretrol.

Raising the pressuretrol setting isn't a good solution to this problem. Overfiring will also throw water up into the piping. This leads to water hammer, uneven heating and short-cycling.

Check your gas pressure, or your nozzle size (on an oil-fired system).

The boiler is making wet steam.

Check the near-boiler piping against the manufacturer's specifications. If the piping can't separate the water from the steam, the water will cause the steam to condense, and the burner will short-cycle.

Check the boiler water's pH and its cleanliness too. You may have to clean the boiler and the system and balance the pH with chemicals.

The steam traps aren't working.

Two-pipe steam is like a ladder. Each radiator is a rung on that "ladder," and at the end of each rung you'll find a steam trap. Part of the trap's job is to keep steam from entering the no-pressure side of the ladder. If even one trap fails in the open position, steam will jump across and pressurize the air on the other side of the system. As the pressure builds, the burner will short-cycle on the pressuretrol.

Float & thermostatic and bucket traps serve the same purpose at the ends of the mains and at the base of risers. If they fail in the open position, or, with bucket traps, if they lose their prime water, steam can move into dry return lines and cause burner short-cycling and water hammer.

Trap maintenance is essential.

The air vents aren't working.

If they're not, the system will trap air and pressurize it. Remember, steam and air are both gases, but steam is lighter than air, so the two won't mix.

117

When the steam heads down a pipe, it pushes air ahead of itself. If the air can't get out at the end of the pipe (through a vent), the steam will just compress it. The pressure builds, and the burner shuts off on the pressuretrol. The burner short-cycles, but that's not your only problem. The building also remains cold because the radiators and mains are filled with air instead of steam. Usually, someone comes along and raises the pressure. They mean well; they're trying to solve the short-cycling and give the folks some heat. But the higher steam pressure just com-presses the air a bit more. It usually doesn't help the lack-of-heat problem. It just raises the fuel bill.

Check the air vents, and clean or replace them where necessary.

The pressuretrol or the pigtail is clogged.

If there's sludge in the pressuretrol or the pigtail that connects the pressuretrol to the boiler, the burner will short-cycle. The pigtail's job is to fill with water and keep the steam temperature from reaching into the pressuretrol. A pigtail is a natural collector of sludge. If you can't clean the pigtail (a tough job), replace it.

The pressuretrol has a mercury switch and it isn't level.

Some pressuretrols have mercury switches. If the pressuretrol isn't plumb and level, the mercury might trip too soon. That can cause the burner to short-cycle.

If the pressuretrol sits on a pigtail, make sure the curved part of the pigtail faces front to back (when you're looking straight at the pressuretrol). If you have the curved part turned from side to side (so you can see through the circle when you're looking straight at the pressuretrol), the burner might short-cycle. This is because the curved part of the pigtail straightens a bit when

119

heated. As it straightens, the pigtail tips the mercury and stops the burner. When you turn the pigtail so that it faces front to back, it tips the pressuretrol from front to back, but not from side to side. This doesn't affect the mercury switch.

THE SYSTEM IS PRODUCING UNWANTED VACUUM.

There are sags in the mains between the boiler and the main vents.

Sags in the main give condensate a place to lay. This creates water hammer when the system starts again, but it can also create vacuum when the boiler shuts off. At very low pressure, steam takes up about 1,700 times the space of water. That's why it does not take much water to fill a system with steam. But when the steam condenses, it turns back into water, shrinking in volume about 1,700 times. If air can't get in to take the place of the shrinking steam, vacuum will form.

121

If there's a sag in the main that fills with condensate, it may be enough to stop the air from reentering the system. If the vacuum is deep enough, it can make the water in the boiler surge up and down. Check the pitch of the pipes with a line level.

The steam pipes are partially insulated.

You're supposed to insulate the supply pipes in a steam system so the steam doesn't condense on its way to the radiators. If some insulation is missing, the steam may be condensing quickly in some areas, and slowly in others. This can create pockets of vacuum within the system, which will cause the steam to flow unevenly.

Insulate all the steam pipes.

There are motorized zone valves near the header.

If a motorized valve in the header piping closes while the boiler is steaming, the steam can't get out of the boiler. When the burner shuts off, the steam that's trapped between the motorized valve and the boiler water line will condense. That condensing action forms a deep vacuum within the boiler. If there's a boiler-feed pump serving the boiler, the vacuum will draw water in from the receiver and flood the boiler.

Install a vacuum breaker in the boiler or the near-boiler piping. Make sure you pipe the vacuum breaker between the boiler water line and the motorized valve.

There are vacuum-type air vents in the system.

In the days of coal-fired boilers, the Dead Men used special air vents that had check valves at their outlets. The check valves let the air out, but they wouldn't let it back in. As a system ran, and the steam condensed, a natural vacuum formed.

The Dead Men used that vacuum to their advantage because in a vacuum, water will boil at a lower temperature. As the coal pile burned down, the energy entering the water lessened. But since the system was in a vacuum, the boiler could still make steam, although it had less fire to work with.

This type of vacuum vent does not work well in an oil- or gas-fired system, however, because the vacuum forms too quickly. Air that can't make its way out on the first cycle will expand greatly and block the flow of the steam to parts of the system.

If you run into this type of vacuum-inducing air vent, replace it with a standard air vent.

THE CONDENSATE- OR BOILER-FEED PUMP DOESN'T ACT AS IT SHOULD.

The strainer is clogged.

There should be a wye or a basket strainer on the inlet to the condensate pump. This strainer's job is to collect sediment from the system before it can get into the condensate pump's receiver. Too much sediment in the receiver will cause problems with the condensate pump.

Someone should clean the strainer at the end of each heating season, but unfortunately, most strainers get cleaned only when there's a problem. If the strainer should clog, little or no condensate will return to the receiver. The condensate pump won't run often enough to replace the water in the boiler. If there's an automatic water feeder on the boiler, it will feed to keep the burner firing. But returning condensate, unable to get through the strainer, will back into the mains and cause water hammer.

Clean the strainer.

There's a lot of sediment in the water.

When was the last time anyone cleaned that system? Steam systems corrode because air enters on every down cycle, and the pipes are usually wet. Particles of rust wash down with the condensate and work their way into the condensate receiver and pump.

The strainer's job is to protect the pump from this sediment. However, if the strainer isn't working (someone may have removed the screen, for instance) particles of rust will work their way into

127

the pump's mechanical seal and cause a leak.

If the condensate pump has a packing gland instead of a mechanical seal (older pumps do), the sediment can cause the gland to leak too much. If you overtighten the packing nut to slow the leak, you might damage the pump's shaft.

Clean the system with trisodium phosphate, and make sure the strainer is clear.

The condensate is too hot for the pump.

As steam traps fail, the returning condensate will get hotter. If the condensate gets too hot (say, near 190 degrees F.), the pump might cavitate when it runs. Cavitation is what happens when a centrifugal pump tries to pump water and the water flashes into vapor. It sounds like gravel is moving through the pump.

This can happen in an open system (such as a steam system) when the water is close to the boiling point. When the impeller spins, the pressure at its inlet drops. The too-hot water flashes into a vapor and expands tremendously. The vapor bubbles then move quickly toward the edge of the impeller where the pressure is high. The higher pressure collapses the vapor bubbles. When that happens, water surrounding the collapsed bubble rushes in to fill the void. This water moves at an incredible speed. It hits the metal at the edge of the pump's impeller with such force that it quickly erodes the metal and causes the pump to fail.

To solve the problem, repair the defective traps. Don't try to cure the problem with a single "master" trap at the inlet to the condensate pump. Get to the root of the problem by repairing the steam traps.

The pH of the water is affecting the pump's mechanical seal.

When the boiler produces steam, the water releases carbon dioxide. This is a result of the carbonates and bicarbonates that you'll find in fresh water. When it's released, the carbon dioxide moves into the system and, if not properly vented, mixes with the condensate on the return side. That creates carbonic acid. Carbonic acid can eat its way through return lines and create leaks. It can also affect the condensate pump's mechanical seal.

Ideally, the pH of a steam system should range between seven (neutral) and nine (mildly alkaline). If the pH gets too low or too high it can affect the ceramic part of the pump's mechanical seal and cause the pump to leak.

Check the water's pH with litmus paper and adjust it with chemicals if necessary.

The boiler pressure is too high.

The condensate pump's job is to put the returning condensate back into the boiler. To do this, the pump has to produce a pressure that's higher than the boiler's operating pressure. As a rule of thumb, if the boiler operates at 50 psi or less, the pump should discharge at the boiler's operating pressure, plus 5 psi. For instance, if you have the boiler set to operate at 2 psi, you'd throttle the condensate pump to discharge at 7 psi. If the boiler operates above 50 psi, the pump should discharge at the boiler's operating pressure, plus 10 psi. So if the boiler were in a dry cleaner's shop producing, say, 90 psi, the pump would have to discharge at 100 psi.

Most condensate pump manufacturers set their standard pumps to discharge at 20 psi. This is good for a low pressure system that can operate up to 15 psi (15 psi + 5 psi = 20 psi). Some condensate pumps, however, are built to order and may have pumps that discharge at a lower pressure. If the pump's pressure can't overcome the boiler's pressure, the pump can't return the condensate to the boiler.

Lower the boiler pressure (if that makes sense), or increase the head pressure of the condensate pump (by replacing it).

The condensate pump's check valve isn't seating tightly.

Since a condensate pump has an atmospheric vent, you have to use a check valve to keep the water in the boiler from flowing backwards into the receiver tank. The check valve goes in the pump's discharge line.

Unfortunately, sludge will often build up in the return line and clog the check valve, keeping it from closing tightly. Make sure you clean that strainer on the condensate- or boiler-feed pump's inlet.

If the check valve doesn't seat tightly, water from the boiler will back up into the receiver, raise the float switch and start the pump. So if you find your condensate- or boiler-feed pump is starting and stopping all the time, take a close look at that check valve. The easiest way to test it is to close the service valve at the inlet to the condensate pump. That will stop the flow of water into the pump's receiver. If the pump continues to cycle on and off, you know the water is coming from the boiler.

Isolate the check valve and clean it out.

The float isn't attached to the float rod.

The float switch in the condensate pump turns the pump's motor on and off. When the receiver fills, the float rises with the water and starts the pump. As the receiver empties, the float senses the falling water and stops the pump's motor.

Now and then, however, the float will work its way off the end

133

of the float rod. When that happens, the pump stops operating because it no longer has a way of knowing where the water is. Usually, the condensate rises up in the receiver's vent or overflow line and floods the boiler room, but don't depend on this. From time to time, a float ball will come off the end of a float rod and work its way into the vent line. If this happens, you might not see the water overflow. Some manufacturers weld a baffle across the vent line inside the tank to keep this from happening.

To check for a missing float ball, operate the float switch by hand. You'll feel the resistance if the float ball is still on the end of the float rod. If it feels too loose, remove the float switch and replace the ball.

There are motorized zone valves near the header.

If a motorized valve closes when there's steam in the boiler, a deep vacuum can form when the steam condenses. Since the condensate pump has an atmospheric vent, the pressure inside the pump's receiver will be higher than the vacuum inside the boiler. Water will flow from the receiver tank into the boiler, and the boiler may flood. If you have a boiler-feed pump, the problem will be very noticeable. That's because a boiler-feed pump has an automatic water feeder in its receiver. The feeder gives the pump an endless supply of fresh water.

You can cure the problem by installing a vacuum breaker anywhere in the near-boiler piping or in the boiler itself. Just make sure the vacuum breaker winds up between the boiler water line and the motorized valves.

There's a "master" trap at the inlet to the condensate pump.

When steam traps fail in the opened position, the returning

condensate eventually will get too hot for the condensate pump to handle. Some contractors who are unfamiliar with steam heating systems will try to solve this problem by installing a single "master" trap at the inlet to the pump's receiver. This creates problems because the return lines are now double-trapped. The flow of condensate back to the boiler will slow, and the boiler will begin to cycle erratically or flood. Remember, the steam traps are in the building to create the points of pressure and no pressure. If the system could work with a single "master" trap, the Dead Man who installed the system would have done it that way.

Another problem with a "master" trap is that it will release condensate at steam temperature. Much of that hot condensate will flash back into steam as it enters the receiver, causing further problems with the pump.

Remove the "master" trap, and repair the defective traps throughout the system.

The voltage supplied to the pump isn't correct.

And if it's not, the pump will either kick a circuit breaker or fuse, or run slowly enough to burn its windings. The electrical power in some areas can be questionable.

If you're having a problem with the motor, check the voltage. If necessary, use a recorder to track any changes in voltage over time. Notify the power company of what you've found.

The boiler room is too hot.

If the motor continually shuts off on its overload protector, check its nameplate for an ambient-temperature rating. Boiler rooms can get extremely hot, and will often exceed the ambient-temperature limits of common electric motors. Find a way to cool the room.

If it's that hot in the boiler room, there's also a good chance you're also not getting enough combustion air to the burners. And keep in mind, some modern boilers draw their combustion air from duct work attached directly to the burner. With little fresh air entering the room, the ambient temperature can get very hot, very fast. Bring in fresh air to cool the room.

The condensate pump discharges into the Hartford Loop.

The Hartford Loop does a good job of protecting the boiler in a gravity-return system. Should a return line spring a leak, water can flow from the wet returns, but not from the boiler because of the Loop.

On a gravity-return system, the wet return connects to the boiler's equalizer at a point about two inches below the lowest operating point (this varies from manufacturer to manufacturer so you should always check their installation instructions).

When you have a condensate pump, you no longer have a gravity-return system. Should a return spring a leak, the boiler water can't back out of the boiler because of the condensate pump's check valve. Should the check valve fail, boiler water will back into the condensate pump. The pump will turn on and pump the water back into the boiler. Should the check valve and the condensate pump fail simultaneously, water will back into the pump's receiver and rise up the vent piping. Since this piping is usually several feet higher than the boiler's water level, the water still can't get out. If there's an overflow pipe in the vent line, however, the condensate can back out of the boiler should both the pump and check valve fail. In this case, a Hartford Loop would help on a pumped return system. But other than that, the Loop may cause problems. Water under pressure from the pump can splash up into the boiler header and create water hammer.

If this is your problem, relocate the pump's discharge line to the bottom of the boiler's equalizer.

The impeller is clogged.

Steam systems are dirty, and condensate vent lines are open to the atmosphere. If sludge works its way into the condensate pump's receiver it can clog the pump's impeller. The pump will cavitate and not move the returning condensate back to the boiler. Water will back up in the system and overflow through the receiver's vent line.

Check the impeller for sludge or other debris by removing the pump from the volute.

The receiver's vent line is plugged.

The vent on a condensate receiver often acts as the air vent for all the system piping. As steam traps fail, the water entering the receiver will get hotter and hotter. Some contractors deal with this by adding a "master" trap at the inlet to the receiver. This is never a good solution.

Other people try to deal with the problem by plugging the receiver's air vent. They figure what they don't see can't hurt them. They're wrong because a condensate pump's receiver can't take much pressure. If you plug the vent, the receiver can explode. That's right, explode.

Another problem is that with a plugged vent line, air can't escape from the system, and condensate will have a tough time making its way back to the boiler room. Now and then, a float ball will come off the end of a float rod and work its way into the vent line. Some manufacturers weld a baffle across the vent line inside the tank to keep this from happening.

If you find a plugged vent line, clear it immediately.

The boiler's water line is priming or surging.

Dirt is usually the culprit here. When you see droplets of water in the part of the gauge glass above the water line, it's time to clean the boiler. If the boiler is priming and surging, it can turn the pump controller on and off. That will make the boiler-feed pump add water when it shouldn't.

Try raising the water line to within an inch of the top of the gauge glass. If the water in the boiler is clean it will not surge over the top of the gauge glass. If it does, clean the boiler with trisodium phosphate.

Also, make sure you're not overfiring the boiler. If you are, correct it by firing only to the connected load.

The pump controller isn't level.

If you have a boiler-feed pump, it's taking orders from the pump controller, which is mounted on the boiler. The pump controller has two factory-adjusted mercury switches. One switch starts and stops the pump in response to the water level in the boiler. The second switch, set to operate at a lower boiler water level, usually serves as a low-water cutoff switch, although you can also use it as an alarm switch. If the pump controller isn't level, the switches may trip too soon or too late, causing the boiler-feed pump to operate erratically.

The wrong pump controller is on the boiler.

McDonnell & Miller supplies many of the pump controllers used in North America. Their most popular pump controller is the #150, and you'll find it on most steam boilers. Since you can use the #150 on boilers rated up to 150 psi, the people at the factory set the control under high-pressure conditions. The high pressure compresses the controller's bellows and affects the vertical distance between the "pump-on" and the "low-water cutoff" points.

If you use the #150 on a low-pressure boiler, however, the bellows will lengthen, and by doing so, shorten the vertical distance between the "pump-on" and "low-water cutoff" points. Working at low pressure, your burner may shut off on low water before the boiler-feed pump has a chance to bring the level up to where it should be.

To avoid (or solve) this problem, order McDonnell & Miller's

#150MD controller instead of their #150 if you have a low-pressure boiler. The "MD" stands for "maximum differential." It's the same control, but McDonnell & Miller sets the "MD" while they have it filled with low-pressure steam. Low-pressure steam doesn't compress the bellows as much, so you wind up with a wider vertical distance between the "pump-on" and "low-water cutoff" points.

Don't try to adjust the factory settings of the mercury switches. If you do, you may void the manufacturer's warranty.

There's no pressure-reducing valve on the feed line to the boiler-feed pump's receiver.

Boiler-feed pumps take their orders from the pump controller, which you'll find mounted on the boiler. The feed pump has a larger receiver than the one you'll find on a condensate pump. The oversized receiver holds enough water to keep the boiler operating

145

during the time it takes for the condensate to return from the system. When the condensate finally does return from the system, it enters the oversized receiver, rather than the boiler. Once there, it waits until the pump controller tells it to enter the boiler.

You'll find a float-operated automatic feed valve in the receiver of most boiler-feed pumps. The feeder's job is to make sure water always fills the lower quarter of the receiver. Typically, these float-operated valves can close off against a city water pressure of about 30 psi. If the city water pressure is higher than that, the valve will pass water, although the valve is supposed to be shut at that point. This can lead to a flooded boiler if the water rises up into the receiver's vent line (static pressure pushes water into the boiler). If there's an overflow line on the vent, you'll spill water either on the floor or down a drain.

If you're having this problem, install a pressure-reducing valve on the supply line going to the automatic feeder. Use the same sort of PRV that you would use to fill a hot water heating system.

THERE'S TOO MUCH HEAT IN THE BUILDING.

The radiators are too big for the space they serve.

There once was a time when people were afraid of the air in a closed room. They thought "vitiated" air (the name they used to describe it) would make them sick so they always kept a window open. The Dead Men knew their clients were going to do this so they compensated by oversizing the radiators on most jobs.

Today, that oversized radiator may be overheating the room it serves. To find out if it is, calculate the heat loss of the room and check this against the size of the radiator. If the radiator is too big, you can solve the problem by installing a thermostatic radiator valve.

If you have a two-pipe system, the TRV replaces the radiator's supply valve. On one-pipe systems, the TRV goes between the air vent and the radiator. This is because you can't throttle the inlet valve on a one-pipe steam radiator.

If you don't want to install a TRV, you can do what the folks who lived during the Victorian era did. Cover the radiator with a heavy-cloth bag, similar to a pillow case. The cloth cuts down on the convective currents and does a good job of undersizing the radiator. The Victorians went out of their way to make their radiator bags decorative. Many of these bags had fringes and a drawstring that would give the Victorians a way of raising and lowering the bag like a curtain.

You can also box in the radiator or use a commercially available radiator cover. Depending on the air pattern it creates, a cover can either increase or decrease the heat output of a radiator.

The steam pressure is too high.

At just under 1 psi, the temperature of steam is about 215 degrees. This is the pressure the Dead Men had in mind when they came up with the charts they used to size steam-heating systems.

To size radiation, they used the term EDR, which stands for Equivalent Direct Radiation. In a steam-heating system, one square foot of EDR will put out 240 BTU/Hr. when there is 70° air outside the radiator and 215° steam on the inside. The Dead Men intended for there to be slightly less than 1 psi in the radiators on the coldest days of the year.

If you raise the pressure, you will also increase the heat that comes from each square foot EDR. For instance, at 10 psi, each square foot EDR puts out 290 BTU/Hr. That's why raising the pressure often overheats the rooms.

Crank it down!

The pipes aren't insulated.

A bare steam pipe will put out about five times the heat of an insulated pipe. When you remove the insulation from a steam pipe, you increase the heat in the room through which the pipe runs. This often happens in basements. Someone removes the asbestos and the basement overheats. The same can happen anywhere in the building.

Insulate the steam pipes.

The thermostat is out of calibration.

If it is, the burner may be running longer than it should. That will quickly overheat all or part of the building. Make sure you use an ammeter when you're checking the thermostat's calibration. Don't guess at that anticipator's setting.

Check, too, to see if the thermostat has a mercury switch. If it does, make sure the thermostat hangs level on the wall. And check to see if the thermostat is in a cold draft, or if it's hanging on a poorly insulated outside wall. Make the necessary corrections.

The device that controls the firing cycle is defective or in the wrong place.

Larger steam-heated buildings have heat-timing devices. These devices will fill the piping and radiation with steam on a call for heat. Then they'll run the boiler for a certain time based on the outdoor temperature.

Some control manufacturers use a pressuretrol to figure out when steam fills the piping and radiation. It's easy to trick a pressuretrol—all it takes is some dirt in either the pressuretrol or the pigtail. If there's too much heat in the building, check that pressuretrol.

Other heat-timing devices use a thermistor to sense temperature rather than pressure. You usually place the thermistor at the end of the longest steam main, but there are no fixed rules; it varies from building to building. However, if the thermistor is on a main that has a clogged air vent, the burner will run all the time. That's because the trapped air will keep the steam from reaching the thermistor.

Check, too, for thermistors that wind up on cold water lines, drain lines and, yes, even gas lines. It happens.

If you have a gravity-return system, make sure the thermistor is high enough on the main. It needs to be below the "A" or "B" Dimension so the rising condensate doesn't cover and cool it. (See *The Lost Art of Steam Heating* for a complete discussion of "A" and "B" Dimensions.)

(Check, too, the sections that follow
for the specific type of system
you're working on.)

Problems that plague
ONE-PIPE STEAM SYSTEMS

THE HEAT IN THE BUILDING IS VERY UNEVEN.

The Dead Men piped the system for a coal burner.

In the days of coal-fired steam boilers the coal pile would burn all day, nudging the steam gently through the pipes and toward the radiators. Knowing that the firing cycle would last at least eight hours and never cycle on and off, the Dead Men often used long perimeter mains to carry the steam from the boiler to the radiators. The main typically followed the foundation wall and dropped below the boiler water line only when it was done wrapping its way around to the basement. From the main, they ran relatively short takeoffs to the radiators.

As oil- and gas-fired systems grew in popularity, the Dead Men

155

faced a problem. Unlike the coal-fired boilers, these new burners cycled on and off. The thermostat often shut off the burner before the steam reached the end of that long main.

To solve their problem, the Dead Men began to pipe their jobs differently. Rather than use a single long main with short takeoffs to the radiators, they used several mains, each heading in a different direction. With these shorter mains, the runs to the radiators usually had to be longer. But that didn't present much of a problem as long as the Dead Men dripped and pitched their lines properly.

If you find yourself facing one of those old, coal-fired piping arrangements, put as many air vents as you can near the end of the main. Your goal is to get the air out of the main quickly so the steam favors that route. If you can fill the main with steam as though it were a long heating trough, you'll do a much better job of balancing the heat throughout the building.

The venting strategy is wrong.

Keep in mind your goal is to heat the building evenly. That means that on the coldest day of the year you want all the radiators to heat all the way across simultaneously. This is a challenge because some radiators are larger than others. Big radiators contain more air than small radiators. If you want a big and a small radiator to heat evenly, you'll have to vent the big radiator more quickly. This is why manufacturers make adjustable air vents, and air vents with various sizes of fixed vent holes.

But some installers get mixed up. They install the quick air vents far from the boiler, and the slow air vents close to the boiler. They don't pay attention to the size of the radiator when they're doing this. You see, if you use main vents, the steam will favor the main and arrive at most of the radiator supply valves simultaneously. That's why you should vent one-pipe radiators in relation to

157

their size, not their location in the building. This is the key to balancing one-pipe steam heat.

The device that controls the firing cycle is defective or in the wrong place.

Larger steam-heated buildings have heat-timing devices. These devices will fill the piping and radiation with steam on a call for heat. Then they'll run the boiler for a certain time based on the outdoor temperature.

Some control manufacturers use a pressuretrol to figure out when steam fills the piping and radiation. It's easy to trick a pressuretrol—all it takes is a dirt in the pressuretrol or pigtail. If the heat in the building is uneven, check that pressuretrol.

Other heat-timing devices use a thermistor to sense temperature rather than pressure. You'd usually place the thermistor at the end of the longest steam main, but there are no fixed rules. It varies from building to building. However, if the thermistor is on a main that has a clogged air vent, the burner will run all the time. That's because the trapped air will keep the steam from reaching the thermistor.

Check, too, for thermistors that wind up on cold water lines, drain lines and, yes, even gas lines. It happens.

If you have a gravity-return system, make sure the thermistor is high enough on the main. It needs to be below the "A" or "B" Dimension so the rising condensate doesn't cover and cool it. (See *The Lost Art of Steam Heating* for a complete discussion of "A" and "B" Dimensions.)

It's a gravity-return system and the ends of the main tie together above the boiler water line.

If steam leaves the boiler and travels in two or more directions through separate mains, those mains will join again at some place in the system. Often they meet on the opposite side of the basement where they drop into a wet return and return to the boiler as a single line.

Steam fills each main because the air escapes through the main vents. Some mains are shorter than others, however, and the steam will usually travel through these more quickly than it will through longer mains. That's why it's important in a gravity-return system that the ends of all the mains join below the boiler water line. If they join above the water line, the steam will zip through the shorter main. It will shut the longer main's air vent before the steam in that pipe can reach the vent. That leads to a very uneven heating system.

The Dead Men used boilers that had higher water lines than you'll find in modern, low-water-content boilers. Their end-of-main piping connections may have come together below the water line of their old boiler, but it might not be the same with your new boiler.

Check your water line against those connections. If you find they're coming together above the water line, drop the returns to the floor and connect them there.

The boiler or the burner is undersized for the radiation.

If the burner is too small for the system, it will run 24 hours a day and not heat the building. It's like putting a pot on simmer. You're putting in enough heat to make the water boil mildly, but not enough to deliver steam to the ends of the mains. Remember, the boiler's ability to produce steam has to match the system's ability to condense steam.

If you suspect the boiler or the burner is too small, measure the radiators in the building, add a suitable pick-up factor for the piping and check it against what's there. The burner must fire to this load as well.

The radiators aren't the right size for the space they serve.

If the radiator is undersized for the space it serves, the room will be cold and the heat will be uneven. Also, look for excessive infiltration. A drafty window can cause many comfort-related complaints that have little to do with the steam system.

The pipes aren't pitched properly.

The pitch of pipes in a one-pipe steam system is crucial. The supply main is also the return main. If you don't quickly get rid of the condensate quickly, it will condense the steam as the steam tries to travel farther down the line. That leads to uneven heating, and very often, water hammer. If the steam travels in the same direction as the condensate, the pitch must be at least one inch in 20 feet. If the steam and condensate flow in opposite directions, you need a minimum pitch of one inch in ten feet. Ideally, you should drip the horizontal runouts to risers. If you can't drip them, pitch them at least one inch per foot back toward the main.

The takeoffs from the main leave at a 90° angle instead of a 45° angle.

Unless you're dripping the riser, the condensate that returns from the radiators has to flow back into the main. It's important to make this connection to the main at a 45° angle so the condensate can hug the side of the horizontal main and flow immediately to the bottom of the main. If the horizontal runout to the riser leaves the main at a 90° angle, the condensate will splash into the flow of steam and keep it from reaching the rest of the radiators. Either get rid of the 90° connection, or drip the base of the riser so the condensate can't return to the main.

There are no drips on the risers.

The condensate from the radiators falls back into the main. This causes the steam to condense before it can fill the rest of the radiators. Add drips to the risers.

If it's a gravity-return system, drip into a wet return or into a loop seal and then to a dry return.

If the job has a condensate- or boiler-feed pump, use a steam trap at the base of the riser drip and flow by gravity from the trap to the pump's receiver.

If you run the system at very low pressure, you can use the loop seals with a dry return instead of the riser traps. But if you do this, keep in mind that if someone raises the system pressure, you'll have water hammer problems and steam at your condensate- or boiler-feed pumps.

The steam quality is bad.

The quality of the steam greatly affects steam distribution.
When steam condenses, it stops traveling. Dirty water or water
with a too-high pH creates wet steam. Look closely at the boiler's
gauge glass. If the steam is dry, the part of the gauge glass above
the water line should be dry as well.

Try raising the water line to within an inch of the top of the
gauge glass. If the water in the boiler is clean it will not surge over
the top of the gauge glass.

Check the pH of the water with pH paper. A good pH for a
steam system is between seven and nine. If the pH gets to 11, the
water will begin to prime and foam and carry over into the system,
causing water hammer. Dead Men often added vinegar to steam
heating systems to lower the pH and improve the steam quality.

If the building heats unevenly, make sure the water is clean.

Someone added something to the water.

What sort of chemicals are they, and how much is in there? Too much of the wrong type of chemical can cause the water's pH to rise, and that will make the water foam. Check the pH, and lower it if necessary.

Did anyone add pipe dope to cure a leak? If so, the boiler is probably producing wet steam. Wet steam doesn't travel far. If the steam can't make it to the far radiators, the building will heat unevenly.

The thermostat is not working, it's in the wrong place, or it's the wrong type of thermostat.

A smaller steam system will usually run off a space thermostat. Typically, the thermostat will be somewhere in the center of the building, but it might also be in the coldest room. If it is in the coldest room, the other rooms might overheat. If the thermostat's in a central location, some rooms might not heat evenly.

Check to make sure you have the thermostat properly calibrated. And use an ammeter when you're checking; don't guess at that anticipator setting. If the thermostat has a mercury switch, make sure it's hanging level on the wall. See if the thermostat is subject to cold drafts or if it's hanging on a poorly insulated outside wall.

The near-boiler piping doesn't meet the manufacturer's specs.

Nowadays, boiler manufacturers consider the near-boiler piping to be a part of the boiler. They use it to help dry the steam before it heads out toward the system. If the near-boiler piping doesn't meet the manufacturer's specs, you could be throwing water up into the piping. This will cause very uneven heating as the steam condenses in the carried-over water.

Get the boiler manufacturer's installation-and-operating manual and check the piping on the job against the drawings in their booklet.

There are no end-of-main air vents.

The key to balancing one-pipe steam systems is to treat the air in the mains differently than you would the air in the radiators. You should vent the mains quickly, and the radiators in proportion to their size.

There should be a large main vent near the end of each main, but not right at the end in a tee. If the main vent is at the end of the main, water hammer might damage it. Place the vent at least 15 inches back from the end of the main, and up on a six-inch nipple. This gets it out of the way of any water hammer damage.

If you vent the mains properly, the steam will travel more evenly through the piping system, and many of your uneven-heating problems will disappear. Missing main vents can also make the burner short-cycle, and this can lead to uneven heat throughout the building.

The end-of-main air vents are clogged with rust and sediment.

When the steam comes up, the air goes out. As these two gasses rush toward the main vents, they carry pieces of rust and sediment with them. Over time, those tiny particles can build up inside the vent and clog it. Remove the vent and see if you can blow through it. If you can't, try boiling it in vinegar for an hour. If that doesn't clear the vent, replace it.

The pipes aren't insulated at all.

A bare steam pipe will put out about five times the heat of an insulated pipe. When you remove the insulation, you increase the

171

heat in that room. This often happens in basements. Someone removes the asbestos and the basement overheats. And since there's only so much heat available from the boiler, most of that heat winds up in the basement. As a result, the building may heat unevenly.

Insulate all steam pipes.

The steam pipes are partially insulated.

You're supposed to insulate the supply pipes in a steam system so the steam doesn't condense on its way to the radiators. If some insulation is missing, the steam may be condensing quickly in some areas and slowly in others. This can create pockets of vacuum that cause the steam to flow unevenly throughout the system.

Insulate all the steam pipes.

The main vents close because water backs into the steam mains.

If your one-pipe steam system has a gravity-return, you have to have at least 28 inches of vertical height between the boiler water line and the bottom of the lowest steam main. We call this the "A" Dimension, and it plays a big part in putting water back into the boiler. If the system doesn't have enough "A" Dimension, returning condensate will back into the main, shut off the main air vents, and create water hammer. If the air can't escape through the main vents, the building will heat unevenly.

There are bullheaded tees on the boiler header or at the ends of the main.

When a steam line enters the bull of a tee, we say that line is bullheaded. Steam and bullheaded tees don't get along well because carried-over condensate usually bounces off the back of the tee and winds up in the distribution piping or the radiator.

Get rid of any bullheaded tee you find in a steam line.

THE AIR VENTS SPIT OR MAKE A HISSING NOISE.

The system is dirty.

Steam heating systems are constantly corroding. The insides of the pipes get wet on each cycle, and then dry out as air rushes back in to fill the void left by the condensing steam. Over time, the pipes rust. Feed water brings in fresh oxygen, which causes corrosion. It also brings in minerals, which build up in the boiler. If no one cleans the system, the rust and mineral deposits, driven by the steam, eventually wind up in the air vents. When a vent can't seat tightly, it will spit water and hiss.

Other vents are not working as they should.

A hissing air vent is trying to tell you something, so listen! The air is rushing to escape because it doesn't have enough ways out of the system. As air vents fail, the velocity of the air leaving the working air vents increases. That's what makes the hissing sound. As the velocity increases, the particles of rust and minerals move more quickly toward the working air vents. Soon, those vents fail as well. If you can hear the vents venting, you don't have enough vents.

Take a good look at the system and clean or replace the clogged air vents.

There are no main vents on the system.

The key to balancing a one-pipe steam system is to vent the air from the mains quickly, and the air from the radiators in proportion to the size of each radiator. If the system has no main vents, the radiator vents have to do two jobs. They'll have to vent the air from both the radiators and the mains. That double duty increases the velocity of the air as it leaves the radiator vents, making them hiss. Inspired by the higher-velocity air, more debris works its way toward the vents, causing them to clog and spit water.

Every one-pipe steam system needs a main vent near the end of each main, but not right at the end in a tee. If the main vent is at the end of the main, water hammer might damage it. Place the vent at least 15 inches back from the end of the main, and up on a six-inch nipple. This gets it of the way of any water hammer damage. If you vent the mains properly, the steam will travel more evenly through the piping system, and leave more slowly through each vent. That increases the life of the vents, and lessens the spitting and hissing problem.

The vents are the wrong size for their location.

There's a lot of air in a steam main so you should use a large vent that can handle a lot of air. If the vent is too small, it will hiss and eventually spit water as it fills with sludge. The same is true for large radiators. They contain a lot of air so you should vent them quickly.

With a large radiator, however, you're better off using two slower air vents instead of one quick one. Drill and tap the radiator for the second vent a few inches below the first vent. The two vents will work together when the steam first reaches the radiator. Then, when the steam reaches the first vent (the higher of the two) the second will continue to vent at a slower rate. Since there will be less air in the radiator at that point, the second vent will be properly sized. This is a Dead Men's trick that works wonders!

The boiler is oversized or overfired.

As you increase the amount of steam moving through a pipe you also increase the steam's velocity. The faster the steam moves, the more likely it will be to drive debris toward the air vents.

Size and fire a boiler to the connected load. No more, and no less.

The system has motorized zone valves.

When a motorized valve shuts, the firing rate of the boiler stays the same. As the boiler tries to move its entire load through the zones left open, the velocity of the steam increases. The faster the steam moves, the more likely it will be to drive debris toward the air vents.

Increase the size of the air vents, or use several main vents on a manifold near the end of each main.

A RADIATOR MAKES A GURGLING SOUND.

The supply valve is partially closed.

In a one-pipe steam system, the steam and the condensate share the same pipe. Steam takes up more space and moves much faster than condensate. The steam and the condensate have to be able to get out of each other's way. That's why a supply valve on a one-pipe steam radiator has to be fully opened during operation. The only reason you'd close it would be to service the radiator, or to shut it off completely.

If the radiator gurgles, make sure the supply valve is fully opened.

The supply valve has come apart.

The valve's handle may turn, but the valve's seat may have come loose from the stem. Remember, this is an old system and it's constantly corroding. Check the valve to make sure the parts are still attached. If they're not, repair or replace the valve.

The radiator is pitched the wrong way.

A one-pipe steam radiator must pitch toward the supply valve so the condensate can drain back to the boiler. Over time, however, the radiator may lose that pitch and this can make it gurgle. This is especially true of radiators that sit on wood floors. The supply pipe supports the radiator only on one side. The other side is left to expand and contract against the wood floor. A cast-iron radiator is heavy, and as the years go by it can dig a trench in the floor. If the radiator's air vent spits, the escaping condensate can soften the wood under the radiator's legs and dig an even deeper trench.

Check the radiator with a six-inch level and make sure it pitches back toward the supply valve. If necessary, shim the radiator.

The radiator is sagging in the middle.

Large cast-iron radiators often sag in the middle. This happens because the condensate that lays in the bottom of the radiator is acidic. It slowly weakens the lower push nipples and causes the radiator to bow in the middle. As water builds in the radiator, the radiator gurgles. This is why it's important to check the pitch of the radiator with a six-inch level. A level this size lets you check

183

the pitch from section to section, not just from end to end.

Correct the sag by shimming the radiator in the center. If the push nipples have corroded to the point where they leak, you'll have to replace them (if you can find replacements).

I've heard of people who have successfully repaired leaks in cast-iron steam radiators with epoxy. Success depends on where the leak is and its severity. If you can't repair the leak, you'll have to replace the radiator.

The radiator has too much pitch.

There's a mud leg at the bottom of a steam radiator. That's the place where sediment accumulates over the years. If you pitch the radiator too much, the sediment will slide toward the supply valve and gather there. Although the supply valve seems to be opened, it will be partially closed by the sediment.

Remove the radiator and flush it out.

The radiator air vent is improperly installed.

An air vent lets the air out, but it also the air back in when the steam condenses. If the air can't get back in, a partial vacuum will form in the radiator, and that will keep the condensate from draining. As the condensate builds, it causes the radiator to gurgle.

Check the air vent. Is it installed sideways or upside down? Some people turn the air vent upside down when they don't want any more heat. Check, too, to see if the air vent is installed on an extension pipe. Condensate may build up inside the air vent and keep it from operating as it should.

Remove the air vent from the radiator and check its tongue. The tongue is the short piece of metal that extends from the vent and hangs inside the radiator. Its job is to drain condensate from the vent. If it's twisted or broken, the vent won't drain and the radiator may gurgle.

185

A RISER IS SLOW TO HEAT.

There's too much radiation attached to the riser.

A steam riser can carry just about any load if you get the pressure high enough, and if you don't care about velocity noise. The challenge with steam heating is to deliver the right load to the radiators using low pressure, usually not more than 2 psi pressure at the boiler.

The Dead Men sized the radiators to heat the space on the coldest day of the year with about 1 psi pressure at the radiator. They used low-pressure steam so the radiators wouldn't overheat and the fuel bills wouldn't soar. They used pipe-sizing charts that showed them the load limits for steam heating (see *The Golden*

Rules of Hydronic Heating). If you connect too much radiation to a steam riser, you won't be able to heat it all unless you raise the pressure to an abnormally high level. And when you raise the pressure, you create other problems: high fuel bills, water level problems at the boiler, and noise.

Check the radiation against the carrying capacity of the pipe. Try closing some radiators to see if that helps. If it doesn't, you may have to repipe.

There's sludge in the horizontal runout to the riser.

This often happens after a one-pipe steam system floods. Water works its way up into the radiators, and the sludge washes down into the horizontal runout to the riser. A puddle of condensate gathers around the sludge, causing the steam to condense. The radiators won't heat properly because the steam can't make it past the sludge and the trapped condensate. If you remove a radiator and shine a light down the riser, you'll see a reflection. That's the trapped water.

Break the riser at its base and flush it from the top under pressure from a garden hose.

The riser needs to be dripped.

In a one-pipe system, all the condensate from the riser and the radiators returns through the horizontal runout to the riser. If too much condensate falls down that riser, the steam won't be able to move toward the radiators.

Drip the line if you can. If you're dripping into a dry return, use either a steam trap or a loop seal.

If you can't drip the riser, increase the size of the horizontal runout to the riser by one size over normal, and pitch it at least one inch per foot back toward the main (see *The Golden Rules of Hydronic Heating* for pipe sizes based on connected load).

THE END-OF-MAIN F&T TRAP IS CAUSING A PROBLEM.

The trap is too small.

In a two-pipe steam system, the end-of-main trap has to handle just the condensate that forms when the main goes from room temperature to steam temperature. Usually, that's not much condensate because the condensate from the radiators returns to the boiler through the radiator traps and separate lines.

Most one-pipe steam systems have gravity returns and no steam traps. But if the system has a condensate- or a boiler-feed pump, the end of the main will need a trap to keep steam from showing up in the receiver. With a pumped, one-pipe system, all the condensate (from both the pipes and the radiators) returns through that single end-of-main F&T trap. You have to size that trap for a much greater load than you would if you were using it on a two-pipe system. Don't base this trap on the line size. Line size may not be big enough in this case.

If the trap is too small, condensate will back into the main and cause water hammer. The water hammer will damage the F&T trap. Check the size of the trap carefully.

The trap isn't sized for the right pressure differential.

A one-pipe steam system operates best at low pressure. To make the end-of-main F&T trap drain quickly, size it for the lowest possible pressure differential. This will give you a larger trap (or a series of traps piped in a manifold), but that larger trap can return the condensate to the boiler quickly. That will keep the condensate from backing up in the system.

There's a water seal between the end-of-main F&T trap and the condensate- or boiler-feed pump.

Air can't vent through a water seal. Take a close look at the line running between the end-of-main F&T trap and the condensate- or boiler-feed pump's receiver. Does the line drop below the level of the receiver's inlet? If it does, you have a water seal. Either correct the piping so it pitches continuously to the receiver's inlet, or install a main vent on the outlet side of the end-of-main F&T trap.

The vent works best on the outlet side of the trap because, in this position, it will serve as both an air vent and a vacuum breaker. That's important because flash steam from the trap can create a partial vacuum between the trap discharge and the water seal. That vacuum can keep condensate from draining. By installing the air vent on the outlet side of the trap, you'll break that vacuum.

THERE'S WATER HAMMER AT THE START OF THE HEATING CYCLE.

The pipes aren't pitched properly.

If condensate lays in the mains between cycles, it will hammer when the steam reaches it on the next cycle. Steam mains must pitch a minimum of one inch in 20 feet when the steam and condensate travel in the same direction. If the steam flows against the condensate, the pipes have to pitch at least one inch in ten feet.

There's a concentric reducer in the steam main.

A concentric reducer will allow condensate to collect if the condensate flows from a large pipe to a small pipe. That causes water hammer at the start of the cycle. Use an eccentric reducer, or drip the main just before it enters the concentric reducer.

194

THERE'S WATER HAMMER IN THE MIDDLE OF THE HEATING CYCLE.

There's not enough vertical space between the boiler water line and the end of the main.

We commonly call this space the "A" Dimension. You need 28 inches of "A" Dimension on a gravity-return, one-pipe steam system. Returning condensate stacks in that space and builds pressure. That pressure combines with the "leftover" steam pressure at the end of the main to put the condensate back into the boiler. If the job doesn't have enough "A" Dimension, water will back into the main and cause water hammer in the middle of the cycle.

This often happens when an installer removes a boiler from a pit and replaces it with a new boiler that's not in the pit. The higher water line of the new boiler shortens the "A" Dimension and causes the water hammer.

Either lower the boiler, or use a condensate- or boiler-feed pump.

The gravity-return lines are clogged.

Clogged returns won't pass condensate. The condensate backs up into the return during the middle of the cycle and creates water hammer at the ends of the mains. Clean or replace the returns.

THERE'S WATER HAMMER NEAR THE END OF THE HEATING CYCLE.

The Hartford Loop isn't piped properly.

Make sure the connection between the return and the equalizer is far enough below the boiler's water line. If steam can work its way down the equalizer and into the wet return it will hammer, and usually at the end of the cycle.

See if there's a long nipple on the Hartford Loop. Long nipples create water hammer as the condensate returns. Replace the long nipple with either a close nipple or a wye fitting.

(Check, too, the Problems that plague ALL STEAM SYSTEMS section.)

197

Problems that plague
TWO-PIPE STEAM SYSTEMS

THERE'S NO HEAT IN PART OF THE SYSTEM.

The steam traps have failed in the closed position.

If a thermostatic radiator trap fails in the closed position, no air will pass through it, so little or no steam will arrive at the radiator.

Open the top of the trap and examine the bellows. If it's cool and fully distended, the trap has probably failed in the closed position. If the system is running when you remove the top of the trap, notice whether air rushes from the radiator. This is another good indication that the trap has failed in the closed position.

Repair or replace the trap.

The steam traps have failed in the open position.

A two-pipe steam system is like a ladder. One side of the ladder is the supply line; the other side is the return line. The rungs of the "ladder" are the radiators, and at the end of each rung there is a steam trap.

The trap's job is to pass air into the return side (the no-pressure) of the ladder, to close when steam arrives, and to reopen when condensate forms. If a trap fails in the open position, steam will pass into the return side of the "ladder," causing water hammer as it meets the condensate. Repair or replace the steam traps.

There's a water leg before the condensate- or boiler-feed pump receiver.

In two-pipe systems, you have steam traps on the radiators instead of air vents. The steam pushes the air through the traps, into the dry returns and toward the condensate- or boiler-feed pump's receiver. Since the receiver is vented to the atmosphere, that's where the air is heading. If your return line drops below the inlet to the receiver, however, you'll have problems. That line isn't under pressure because it's downstream of the radiator and end-of-main F&T traps. As condensate drains from the radiators and pipes, it will pool in that water leg and form a seal. Air can't vent through that water seal, so the building will take forever to heat.

If the traps are defective, they'll mask this problem because there will be enough pressure to force the condensate out of the water leg. A lot of water hammer usually accompanies this evacua-

201

tion of the water. That encourages the building owner to have his traps fixed. When you fix the traps he'll have no heat because the air can't get out. At this point, you have two choices. Raise the return line to eliminate the water seal, or install main vents at the outlet side of the end-of-main F&T traps.

THE BOILER GOES OFF ON LOW WATER.

The water backs out of the boiler.

This problem often pops up with a gravity-return (no condensate- or boiler-feed pump) system. If the boiler pressure is more than the "B" Dimension can overcome, the water will back into the return lines, and often cause water hammer at the ends of the main. The water hammer can damage the steam traps. (See *The Lost Art of Steam Heating* for a discussion of "B" Dimensions.)

If the boiler has an automatic water feeder, the feeder will add water. At the end of the heating cycle, the condensate will return from the system, and since the feeder added water, the boiler will flood. Try lowering the pressure.

And keep in mind, the Dead Men designed most gravity-return, two-pipe systems to run well at extremely low pressure (typically in ounces). If you can't heat the building at low pressure, the system is probably air-bound. Check your air vents.

THE MAIN VENTS SQUIRT WATER.

They're either in the wrong place, or they're dirty.

You'll find end-of-main vents near the ends of the mains on gravity-return, two-pipe systems. You'll also find them near the bottoms of the return risers. Make sure the vents aren't in a place where water hammer can reach them. Ideally, they should be at least 15 inches back from the end of the main, and at least six inches up on a nipple.

Since gravity-return systems have no vented condensate- or boiler-feed pumps, the only way for air to escape is through the main vents. If the boiler pressure is too high, water will back into the vents and make them squirt. Crank the pressure down, and you should see a difference immediately.

Also, since the water leaves sediment in the main vents, you may have to boil the vents in vinegar for an hour to clean them out. If that doesn't work, the vents may have been damaged by water hammer. Replace them.

THE BURNER SHORT-CYCLES.

The pressure is too high.

If it's a gravity-return, two-pipe system, high boiler pressure will back water up into the vents, and trap air in the system. Many of the radiators won't heat. And since air is a compressible gas (just like steam), the burner will begin to short-cycle as the steam squeezes the air into a corner. You may be tempted to increase the pressure, thinking this will cure the short-cycling. But don't do it; it will only make things worse. Instead of cranking the pressure up, crank it down. And think like air. Walk along the piping and ask yourself, If I were air, could I get out? If you can't get out, neither can the air.

207

The burner is overfiring.

Overfiring can also cause the burner to short-cycle. Fire only to the connected piping and radiation load—no more and no less.

The steam quality is poor.

Wet steam also can cause short-cycling. The steam leaves the boiler, the pressuretrol hits its high limit, the steam rapidly condenses and causes the burner to turn back on.

The water is dirty.

Dirty water is another common cause of burner short-cycling. Clean the system with trisodium phosphate.

TWO-PIPE

THERE'S STEAM COMING OUT OF THE CONDENSATE- OR BOILER-FEED PUMP'S RECEIVER.

The steam traps have failed in the open position.

Besides causing water hammer and uneven heating throughout the building, steam will show up in the vented receiver when the traps fail. As the condensate gets hotter, the condensate- or boiler-feed pump will begin to cavitate. Before long, the pump can't move the water, and the receiver overflows.

Find the failed traps and repair or replace them.

There's a "master" trap at the inlet
to the condensate pump.

When steam traps fail in the system, the returning condensate will be too hot for the condensate pump to handle. Some contractors who are unfamiliar with steam heating systems will try to solve this problem by installing a single "master" trap at the inlet to the pump's receiver. This creates problems because the return lines are now double-trapped. The flow of condensate back to the boiler will slow, and the boiler will begin to cycle erratically or flood.

Remember, the steam traps are in the building to create the points of pressure and no pressure. If the system could operate with a single "master" trap, the Dead Man who installed the system would have done it that way.

Another problem with a "master" trap is that it will release condensate at steam temperature. Much of that hot condensate

211

will flash back into steam as it enters the receiver, causing further problems with the pump.

Remove the "master" trap, and repair the defective traps throughout the system.

The steam traps are oversized.

If you base the size of the two-pipe steam trap on the size of the line, you will almost always oversize the trap. An oversized trap will barely open when the condensate reaches it. Since the pin sits so close to the seat of the barely opened trap, the condensate will flow across the seat at high velocity. Condensate contains bits of rust and sediment, which quickly wear down the seat, keeping the trap from shutting tightly. Trap manufacturers call this process "wire drawing," and it's a very common cause of trap failure.

Check the size of the trap against the load and the pressure differential. If it's oversized, replace it.

THERE'S WATER HAMMER AT THE START OF THE HEATING CYCLE.

The pipes aren't pitched properly.

If condensate lays in the mains between cycles, it will hammer when the steam reaches it on the next cycle. Steam mains must pitch a minimum of one inch in 20 feet when the steam and condensate travel in the same direction. If the steam flows against the condensate, the pipes have to pitch at least one inch in ten feet.

There's a concentric reducer in the steam main.

A concentric reducer will allow condensate to collect if the condensate flows from a large pipe to a small pipe. That causes water hammer at the start of the cycle.

Use an eccentric reducer, or drip the main just before it enters the concentric reducer.

The steam traps have failed in the open position.

A two-pipe steam system is like a ladder. One side of the ladder is the supply line; the other side is the return line. The rungs of the ladder are the radiators, and at the end of each rung there is a steam trap. The trap's job is to pass air into the return side (the no-pressure) of the "ladder", to close when steam arrives, and to reopen when condensate forms. If a trap fails in the open position, steam will pass into the return side of the "ladder," causing water hammer as it meets the condensate.

Repair or replace the steam traps.

THERE'S WATER HAMMER IN THE MIDDLE OF THE HEATING CYCLE.

**In a gravity-return system,
there's not enough vertical space
between the boiler water line
and the lowest steam trap.**

We call a two-pipe system that doesn't have a condensate- or boiler-feed pump a gravity-return system. The only force available to put the condensate back into the boiler is the static weight it creates as it stacks in the vertical space between the boiler water line and the lowest steam trap.

This is very different from what happens in a gravity-return, one-pipe system. In a one-pipe system, you have steam at the end of the main. The steam works with the static pressure of the returning condensate in the "A" Dimension to put the condensate back into the boiler. The "A" Dimension is the vertical space between the boiler water line and the bottom of the lowest steam-carrying pipe. It must be at least 28 inches.

In a two-pipe system, however, there is no steam at the ends of the main because of the steam traps. All you have going for you is the static weight of the water between the boiler water line and the lowest steam trap. We call this the "B" Dimension. Since a column of water 28 inches high exerts a pressure of 1 psi at its bottom, we need a bit more than 28 inches of water in the "B" Dimension for every pound of pressure in the boiler. Without this pressure, the condensate can't return.

So in a gravity-return system, if you have a boiler pressure of 2 psi, you'd have to have at least 60 inches of stacking space in your "B" Dimension. Raise the pressure and you'll need even more space in the "B" Dimension.

If the condensate is not returning to the boiler, try lowering the

TWO-PIPE

boiler pressure. If this doesn't work, you may need a condensate- or boiler-feed pump.

The gravity-return lines are clogged.

Clogged returns won't pass condensate. The condensate backs up into the return during the middle of the cycle and creates water hammer at the ends of the mains.

Clean or replace the returns.

The steam traps have failed in the open position.

A two-pipe steam system is like a ladder. One side of the ladder is the supply line; the other side is the return line. The rungs of the ladder are the radiators, and at the end of each rung there is a steam trap. The trap's job is to pass air into the return side (the no-pressure) of the "ladder", to close when steam arrives, and to reopen when condensate forms. If a trap fails in the open position, steam will pass into the return side of the "ladder," causing water hammer as it meets the condensate.

Repair or replace the steam traps.

The end-of-main or base-of-riser F&T traps have failed in the closed position.

A float & thermostatic trap has a mechanical float that responds to water level. When the trap fills with condensate, the float rises and lifts the valve's pin from its seat so condensate can flow into the returns.

Water hammer can damage the F&T trap's float, crushing it or

219

putting a hole in it so that it fills with water. Once the float fills with water, the trap can't release its condensate. Water backs up in the mains and causes water hammer.

Check the F&T traps by opening a valve or a union downstream of the trap and watching what comes out. If the trap isn't working, repair or replace it.

The end-of-main F&T traps are the wrong size.

In a pumped-return system, there should be an F&T trap at the end of each main. The trap has three jobs: to allow air to pass through to the condensate- or boiler-feed pump where it can vent from the system, to close when steam reaches the end of the main, and to open when condensate reaches the trap. If the trap is too small, it can't get rid of the condensate quickly enough. The condensate will back into the main and create water hammer.

When you size an F&T trap, you have to consider the condensate load and the pressures on the inlet and outlet sides of the trap (the differential pressure). Don't go by line size. The size of the seat (the hole) inside an F&T trap will vary with the differential pressure. The higher the pressure, the smaller the hole, and vice versa. If you use a high-pressure trap on a low-pressure system, the trap's seat will be too small to handle the condensate. You'll have water hammer at the ends of the mains.

Check the trap size, and the size of the trap's seat against the load (see *The Lost Art of Steam Heating* for the procedure for sizing end-of-main F&T traps).

TWO-PIPE

THERE'S WATER HAMMER NEAR THE END OF THE HEATING CYCLE.

The Hartford Loop isn't piped properly.

Make sure the connection between the return and the equalizer is far enough below the boiler's water line. If steam can work its way down the equalizer and into the wet return, it will hammer, and usually at the end of the cycle.

Check, too, for a long nipple on the Hartford Loop. Long nipples create water hammer as the condensate returns. Replace the long nipple with either a close nipple or a wye fitting.

The condensate- or boiler-feed pump discharges into a Hartford Loop.

The Hartford Loop does a good job of protecting the boiler in a gravity-return system. Should a return line spring a leak, water can flow from the wet return, but because of the Loop, it can't flow from the boiler.

On a gravity-return system, the wet return connects to the boiler's equalizer at a point about two inches below the lowest operating point. This varies from manufacturer to manufacturer so you should always check their installation instructions.

When you have a condensate pump, you no longer have a gravity-return system. Should a return spring a leak, the boiler water can't back out of the boiler because of the condensate pump's check valve. Should the check valve fail, boiler water will back into the condensate pump. The pump will turn on and pump

TWO-PIPE

the water back into the boiler. Should the check valve and condensate pump fail simultaneously, water will back into the pump's
receiver and rise up the vent piping. Since this piping is usually
several feet higher than the boiler's water level, the water still
can't get out.

If there's an overflow pipe in the vent line, however, the
condensate can back out of the boiler, should both the pump and
check valve fail. In this case, a Hartford Loop would help on a
pumped return system. But other than that, the Loop may cause
problems. Water under pressure from the pump can splash up into
the boiler header and create water hammer. If this is your problem,
relocate the pump's discharge line to the bottom of the boiler's
equalizer.

(Check, too, the Problems that plague
ALL STEAM SYSTEMS section.)

Problems that plague
MECHANICALLY INDUCED
VACUUM SYSTEMS

THE BUILDING HEATS UNEVENLY.

The vacuum pump isn't producing the right vacuum.

In a heating system, a vacuum pump usually produces vacuum in a range of three to eight inches of mercury. If the pump has to lift condensate from a low point, either through lift fittings or an accumulator tank, the pump must produce an additional inch of mercury vacuum for every foot of vertical lift.

If the condensate is too hot (because of failed steam traps) or if the system has leaks, the vacuum pump won't produce the vacuum you need to move steam quickly through the system. Check the temperature of the returning condensate. Ideally, it shouldn't be hotter than 180 degrees.

To check the vacuum pump's operation, close the inlet valve to the vacuum pump's receiver. If the pump starts to pull vacuum with the valve closed, look for leaks in the system. Check to see if someone added vacuum breakers or air vents anywhere in the system.

The system might also have a condensate transfer pump at a low point. We use these pumps instead of less reliable accumulator tanks and lift fittings. The vent line on the transfer pump's receiver has to connect into a dry return line, downstream of the steam traps. If someone left the vent line open to atmosphere, the vacuum pump won't produce vacuum.

Make sure the vacuum pump has enough hurling water. This is the water in the upper chamber of the vacuum pump. Without hurling water, the vacuum pump can't produce vacuum. You'll find a float switch in the upper chamber. The float switch operates the solenoid valve that admits the hurling water. Check both the switch and the solenoid valve.

 **THE BOILER FLOODS.**

The system has a vacuum pump and a boiler feed pump.

When you replace an old boiler with a new boiler, you sometimes need to use a boiler-feed pump. The boiler-feed pump acts as a reservoir to hold the water that used to be in the old boiler, but isn't in the new boiler. The boiler-feed pump's job is to keep the boiler from flooding, and from shutting down on low water.

If the Dead Man sized the system's pipes, valves, fittings and steam traps for a pressure-to-vacuum differential, you have to use a vacuum pump. Without the vacuum pump, steam won't flow quickly from the boiler to the radiators. You'll have to use higher-than-normal pressure and the system will heat unevenly.

228

When you have both a vacuum pump and a boiler-feed pump, the boiler-feed pump will be closest to the boiler. When the vacuum pump starts, it will pull vacuum right back to the boiler. As the vacuum forms in the boiler, atmospheric pressure inside the boiler-feed pump will push water into the boiler, causing the boiler to flood.

To solve the problem, install a motorized valve on the boiler-feed pump's discharge line. Use the boiler-mounted pump controller to operate the motorized valve, and have the valve start the boiler-feed pump through its end switch.

The condensate returns too slowly.

A vacuum pump operates like a condensate pump. When its receiver fills, the vacuum pump returns the water to the boiler. The vacuum pump has no way of knowing whether the boiler needs this water.

229

If some steam traps have failed, the condensate will return more slowly because there will be less pressure differential between the mains and the returns. The automatic water feeder will add water to keep the boiler operating. When the condensate finally does return to the vacuum pump, the pump will add it to the boiler, and the boiler will flood.

If the steam traps have failed in the open position, steam will pass into the return lines and heat the condensate. The vacuum pump can't pump water when it's that hot. The pump cavitates, and little or no water flows back to the boiler. If there's no automatic water feeder on the job, the boiler will go off on low water.

THERE'S WATER HAMMER IN THE RETURNS.

The dry returns aren't pitched properly.

The vacuum pump's main job is to remove air from the system, not to return condensate to the boiler. As in a pressure system, water should return to the boiler by gravity. If the pitch on the returns isn't continuously downhill, condensate will accumulate in the returns. Depending on the system pressure, flash steam from the steam traps can enter the returns when the traps open. The flash steam will create water hammer when it meets the accumulated condensate in the returns.

Correct the pitch.

(Check, too, the Problems that plague
*   ALL STEAM SYSTEMS section*
*   and the Problems that plague*
TWO-PIPE STEAM SYSTEMS section.)

Problems that plague
VAPOR and VAPOR/VACUUM
SYSTEMS

(First, a definition: These are the one- and two-pipe systems the Dead Men installed during the early days of this century. A vapor system operates between zero psi and eight ounces of pressure. A vapor/vacuum system operates between any level of vacuum and eight ounces of pressure.)

INDIVIDUAL RADIATORS DON'T HEAT WELL.

The device on the radiator return is clogged with rust, sludge and sediment.

In the days of vapor and vapor/vacuum heating, the Dead Men used several devices on the return side of their radiators to keep steam out of the returns. This was during a time when thermostatic radiator traps were still new. The Dead Men liked these return devices because they had so few moving parts.

For instance, a common return device was a simple union elbow with a built-in orifice. The orifice would allow only so much steam into the radiator. The Dead Men then sized the radiator to

234

condense at least that amount of steam. Sure, some steam entered the return, but not much. Most of it would condense in the radiator. What flowed across the orifice was mostly condensate.

Some devices had a small water seal that was about an inch deep. The water seal would condense any vapor that made it through the radiator. The Dead Men could get away with this because they ran their vapor and vapor/vacuum systems at very low pressure, usually less than eight ounces. There was a small hole above the water seal in the return device. Air passed through this hole and vented at the end of the dry return. If dirt clogs that tiny hole, the radiator won't heat properly. The return device has a small plug that you can remove to get at the air hole.

Other return devices had a small metal ball that moved toward the radiator, following the partial vacuum that formed as steam condensed inside the radiator. When the level of condensate inside the radiator rose high enough, it pushed the metal ball back and allowed the condensate to drain. If you take this device apart to clean it, don't lose that ball! These devices also had inch-deep water seals to condense any vapor that made it that far.

There was a return device that had a weighted check valve. Condensate would have to build up inside the radiator before the check valve would open. The weight in the check valve gave the Dead Men the pressure differential they needed from the supply to the return.

There were also orificed inlet valves. These valves allowed only so much steam into the radiator. Here again, the Dead Men sized the orifice to the radiator's ability to condense steam.

If any of these devices clogs with sediment, rust or sludge, the radiator won't heat well. Carefully take the device apart and clean it. If the device is damaged, replace it with a thermostatic steam trap.

If you have to remove an orificed supply valve, replace it with a standard supply valve, but add a thermostatic steam trap to the radiator. If the radiator already has a thermostatic radiator trap, check to see if it's failed in the closed position. If the trap is working, check nearby traps to see if they have failed. If they have, they're probably pressurizing the return line, and that's locking the air in your problem radiator.

THERE'S STEAM COMING FROM THE CHIMNEY.

There's a hole in the boiler.

This happens to cast-iron boilers when they take on a lot of fresh feed water. The oxygen boils out of the water and eats a hole through the metal, usually right at the boiler's water line. The water steams off and goes up the flue. You can't see it unless you're looking at the chimney. It looks like white smoke, but it's not smoke; it's water vapor.

To check for a hole, flood the boiler up into the header piping. You'll know you have a problem if you see water pouring out of the boiler's jacket. If there's a hole in the boiler you'll never build pressure, and you may not be able to heat the building to the ends of

237

the run either.

You'll have to replace the damaged section to fix this one.

The boiler pressure is too high.

With some vapor and vapor/vacuum systems, the Dead Men ran the dry return through a radiator that hung from the boiler room ceiling. This radiator served as a condenser. Any steam vapor that made it that far into the system would turn to water inside the condensing radiator, and drain back into the boiler.

From the condensing radiator, the dry return vented into the chimney. The Dead Men used the chimney draft to pull the air through the system. These systems were limited to very low pressure, usually about six ounces. If the pressure went above that point, a relief valve would pop.

If someone removed any of the original vapor or vapor/vacuum equipment and installed a new boiler, the pressure might be too high. That's why you're seeing steam coming from the chimney.

If the boiler has a pressuretrol, remove it and replace it with a vaporstat. A vaporstat lets you operate the boiler in ounces of pressure. Crank the pressure down to six ounces or so, and the steam should stop coming out of the chimney.

THE HEAT IS NOT EVEN THROUGHOUT THE SYSTEM.

The pressure is too high.

If the system has return devices (P-traps, weighted check valves, vacuum balls, orifices), higher-than-necessary steam pressure will push through and enter the return. Once that happens, the pressure in the return will approach the pressure in the supply and the steam will slow. Any air that didn't vent from the radiators will find itself trapped until the next cycle.

Crank the pressure down. Use a vaporstat instead of a pressuretrol. Vapor and vapor/vacuum systems want to run at extremely low pressure. Accommodate them.

Thermostatic radiator traps
have failed in the open position.

If the traps on the radiators or at the ends of the main fail in the open position, steam will enter the return lines. Once there, it will equalize the pressures on the supply and return sides of the system. When that happens, the flow of steam stops.

Check the thermostatic radiator traps with a thermometer. There should be at least a 10° temperature difference from one side to the other. If you don't see a temperature difference, repair or replace the traps.

VAPOR/VACUUM

The loop seals at the ends of the main are too high compared with the new boiler's water line.

Vapor and vapor/vacuum systems usually have a steam main, a dry return main (from the radiators), and a wet return (from the ends of the steam mains). The steam mains and the dry return mains often pitch in the same direction, that is, away from the boiler. They then tie together at their ends with a loop seal that keeps steam from entering the dry return.

The bottom of the loop seal connects into the wet return. From there, all the condensate flows back to the boiler. Since the bottom of the loop seal drains into the wet return, the Dead Men had to be very careful with one detail. They had to make sure the point where the dry return and the steam main came together was below the boiler's water line. If it was above the boiler water line, steam would dip down from the end of the main and flow through the loop seal into the dry return. Once that happened, the steam would stop moving because there would be very little difference in pressure between the supply and return sides of the system.

Now, let's say someone installs a replacement boiler. That new boiler probably has a lower water line than the boiler it's replacing. If the water line is too low, the loop seal will go dry and steam will enter the dry return.

Solve the problem by dropping the loop seal below the water level of the new boiler.

The end-of-main vent/traps have failed either open or closed.

The Dead Men didn't like to use a lot of air vents. They preferred to use just one very large vent, and it was usually in the boiler room, at the end of the dry return. Steam would push the air through the main, into the radiators, across the radiator traps, into the dry return and back to the large air vent.

The problem, though, was that the radiator closest to the boiler would always heat first, and the radiator farthest from the boiler would always heat last. To get around this, the Dead Men installed a half-inch thermostatic radiator trap at the end of the steam main. This trap, which was always higher than the main, acted as an air vent. Air would pass through it and enter the dry return where it would continue to that large air vent.

With the vent/trap at the end of the main, steam would favor the main before entering the radiators because that was the path of least resistance. Steam would leave the boiler and fill the main as though it were a trough. From there, the steam would enter each radiator simultaneously.

The end-of-main vent/trap is crucial to even heating in a vapor or vapor/vacuum system. If the vent/trap fails in the closed position, the radiator closest to the boiler will heat first, while the radiator farthest from the boiler heats last. If the vent/trap fails in the open position, steam will enter the dry return and pressurize it.

With little difference in pressure between the supply and the return, the building will heat unevenly, and some airbound radiators won't heat at all.

Check the temperature difference across the vent/trap. It should be at least ten degrees Fahrenheit. If it's not, repair or replace the trap.

The wet return is clogged.

If the return line is clogged, condensate will back up and cover either an air vent or the thermostatic steam trap at the end of the steam main that acts as an air vent. If the air can't get out, the steam can't get in, and the building will heat very unevenly.

245

The vacuum is too deep.

Vapor/vacuum systems produce vacuum naturally. The steam pushes the air out of a very large main vent, which you'll find at the end of the dry return. The vent has a check valve at its outlet. The check valve keeps the air from returning to the system.

There were also one-pipe vapor/vacuum systems that had these special air vents on the radiators. Both the one- and two-pipe versions of this system were beneficial during the days of coal-burning boilers. Late in the day, when the coal pile burned down, there was less energy going into the water. By putting the system under vacuum, the Dead Men could keep the water boiling at a lower temperature. It worked well because the vacuum would form gradually over the course of a full day.

Modern oil or gas burners, however, do something coal burners didn't do: They cycle on and off, and this often causes a problem because the vacuum can form before all the air is out of the system. Any air trapped in the radiators will expand tremendously when the vacuum forms. The expanded air will keep the steam vapor from reaching the radiators and leave you with a building that heats unevenly.

If this is your problem, remove the check valve from the air vent, or replace the air vents at the end of the main or on the radiators with modern vents that don't produce a vacuum.

The chimney line is clogged.

If you have an old vapor system that vents air into the chimney, check the line. Loosen the pipe plug on the tee you'll find at the point where the pipe enters the chimney. If the line is clogged, the system won't vent properly. If you find you're running higher-than-normal pressure (normal is about six ounces), check the line. It's probably clogged with debris from the chimney. Clear the line.

THE BOILER EITHER GOES OFF ON LOW WATER OR IT FLOODS.

The return is clogged with sludge.

Vapor and vapor/vacuum systems have wet and dry returns. Dry returns usually don't clog because they carry only air and condensate. On the other hand, condensate always fills the wet return, making it prone to a buildup of rust, sediment and sludge. If the wet return clogs, some condensate will return to the boiler through the dry returns, but not all of it. This leads to water level problems at the boiler.

While it waits for the slowly returning condensate from the clogged wet return, the automatic water feeder might feed. When the condensate eventually makes its way back from the system, the boiler will flood.

Clean or replace the wet return.

The boiler return trap isn't working as it should.

The boiler return trap's job is to put the condensate back into the boiler. It doesn't come on line when the boiler pressure is low. But as boiler pressure starts to build, the condensate may not have enough "B" Dimension to get back into the boiler.

Below the boiler return trap, in the wet return, you'll find two check valves. The boiler return trap's line enters the wet return between those two check valves. When the boiler pressure builds, the inboard check valve (the one closest to the boiler) will close. The returning condensate now has no choice other than to go up the line into the boiler return trap.

Once inside the trap, the condensate lifts a float ball and opens a valve to a steam line. The steam enters the top of the boiler return trap. Once there, it combines with the static weight of the condensate to close the outboard check valve and open the inboard check valve. The condensate goes back into the boiler.

As the float ball falls, it closes the steam line and opens an equalizing line back to the dry return. On the next cycle, the process repeats.

If the boiler return trap isn't working, condensate won't return to the boiler. Clean it, or replace it with a boiler-feed pump (see *The Lost Art of Steam Heating* for full instructions on how to do this).

The wet return check valves are clogged.

If either the inboard or the outboard check valve gets stuck either open or closed, the water won't return to the boiler. If the boiler is going off on low water, or if it's flooding (through an automatic water feeder), suspect the check valves. Take them apart and clean them out.

THE BURNER SHORT-CYCLES.

The vaporstat is set wrong.

Most vapor and vapor/vacuum systems run best on a vapor-stat. Unlike a pressuretrol, a vaporstat regulates the system pressure in a tight range between zero and 16 ounces.

Start by setting the vaporstat to cut in at four ounces and cut out at 12 ounces. Since a vaporstat's differential setting is subtractive, you should set the "Main" at 12 ounces and the "Differential" at eight ounces. Set that way, the boiler will cut in at four ounces and cut out at 12 ounces.

Experiment with the cut-out pressure after you have the system running. Crank it down in one-ounce increments. If you're able to get steam to the farthest radiator on less pressure, do it. The lower

251

the pressure, the better the old vapor or vapor/vacuum system will operate.

The cross-over vent trap isn't working.

If steam passes into the dry return before the air gets out of the radiators, pressure will build, and the burner will shut off on the pressuretrol or the vaporstat. Since there won't be much steam in the system when this happens, the steam will quickly condense and drop the pressure. The pressuretrol or vaporstat will start the burner, repeating the process. The burner will short-cycle every few minutes.

Check the end-of-main vent trap with a thermometer. If it's not working, repair or replace it.

Steam traps have failed in the open position.

Open the large vent at the end of the main. You shouldn't have any steam coming from it. If you do, one or more steam traps have failed in the open position. They're pressurizing the dry return line and trapping air in the system. The trapped air is causing the burner to short-cycle.

Find the defective traps and repair or replace them.

The central air eliminator is clogged.

The central air eliminator, that large air vent at the end of the dry return, is the only place air can escape from a vapor or a vapor/vacuum system. Over time, rust and sediment will build up

253

in the vent and clog it. If the air can't get out, the steam will quickly compress it, making the pressuretrol or vaporstat stop the burner. As the steam condenses, the pressuretrol or vaporstat will start the burner again.

Check the central air eliminator for dirt. Clean or replace it.

The boiler return trap is missing.

A boiler return trap looks like a very large steam trap. Now and then, an installer will replace an old boiler return trap with a large F&T trap, thinking they do the same thing. They don't. A boiler return trap does what a condensate pump does: It puts the returning condensate back in the boiler. An F&T trap keeps steam from crossing from a steam line into a dry return line.

If someone took out the boiler return trap and didn't replace it with either a condensate- or a boiler-feed pump, the condensate won't return to the boiler. It will back into the dry return mains, close the central air eliminator and trap the air in the system. The trapped air will make the burner short-cycle.

If you install a condensate- or boiler-feed pump, make sure you also install F&T traps at the ends of the steam mains.

Insulation is missing from the steam mains.

If steam leaves the boiler and enters uninsulated pipe, the steam will quickly condense. As it condenses, the burner begins to short-cycle on the pressuretrol or the vaporstat.

Since they operate on such low pressures, vapor and vapor/vacuum systems are especially prone to this mistake. Insulate the steam mains.

(Check, too, the Problems that plague
ALL STEAM SYSTEMS section
and the Problems that plague
TWO-PIPE STEAM SYSTEMS section.)

Problems that plague
COMMERCIAL STEAM
SYSTEMS

THE HEAT EXCHANGER'S TUBE BUNDLE LEAKS.

There's no vacuum breaker in the heat exchanger's shell.

When steam enters a shell-and-tube heat exchanger it quickly condenses on the outside surfaces of the tubes. This happens because there's a fluid that's cooler than steam inside the tubes.

As the steam condenses, it leaves a partial vacuum in its place. This is especially true if there's a control valve on the heat exchanger's steam inlet. If you don't have a vacuum breaker in the shell, the condensate won't drain from the heat exchanger's shell. On the next cycle, the steam will meet the undrained condensate and cause water hammer.

The violent hammering takes place at the far end of the heat exchanger, opposite the fluid inlet and outlet. Fluids don't compress, so when they hit the back end of the shell, they bounce off and pummel the rounded end of the tube bundle. This can make the tube bundle leak.

Install a vacuum breaker in the shell of the heat exchanger.

THERE'S WATER HAMMER IN THE HEAT EXCHANGER.

Condensate isn't draining from the heat exchanger.

A steam trap's job is to stay open on start-up so the air can pass, to close when steam arrives, and to open when condensate forms. To size the trap, you have to consider the load and the pressure difference between the supply and return sides of the heat exchanger. If the traps are too small, condensate will back into the heat exchanger (whether it's a steam-to-air exchanger or a steam-to-liquid exchanger). As the steam and the condensate come together, you'll get water hammer.

Check the size of the trap. Make sure you're considering the right pressure differential across the trap.

If there's a control valve, size the trap for the minimum pressure differential because that's what you'll get when the control valve throttles and closes.

Make sure you allow for as much vertical distance as possible between the bottom of the heat exchanger and the steam trap. The idea is to give the condensate a place to gather ahead of the trap where it can build static pressure. If there's a control valve on the heat exchanger, that static pressure might be the only thing you have going for you when it comes time to push the condensate through the trap.

There's no vacuum breaker on the steam side of the heat exchanger.

When steam enters a heat exchanger it quickly condenses and leaves a partial vacuum in its place. This is especially true if there's a control valve on the heat exchanger's steam inlet. If you don't have a vacuum breaker on the steam side, condensate won't drain from the heat exchanger. On the next cycle, the steam will meet the undrained condensate and cause water hammer.

Install a vacuum breaker on the steam side of the heat exchanger.

THE HEAT EXCHANGER WON'T HEAT COMPLETELY.

There's air trapped in the heat exchanger.

Besides a vacuum breaker, there should also be an air vent on the steam side of the heat exchanger. If air can't get out, steam can't get in. The vent must be on the outlet, not the inlet side of the exchanger.

If there's a steam trap on the exchanger, make sure air can pass through the trap and vent somewhere downstream. Check for water seals downstream of the trap. You'll often find a water seal where the condensate return drops below the inlet to the condensate- or boiler-feed pump's receiver. Air can't vent through a water seal.

Look the situation over carefully and ask yourself, If I were air, could I get out? If you can't get out, neither can the air. Provide a vent.

Two heat exchangers share the same steam trap.

Each heat exchanger (whether it's a steam-to-air exchanger or a steam-to-fluid exchanger) needs its own steam trap. Some installers try to save money by having two heat exchangers share one steam trap, but this simply won't work. Steam passes through one heat exchanger (the one with the lower pressure drop), closes the air vent, and air-locks the other heat exchanger. You can't get the steam to pass equally through both heat exchangers, no matter how carefully you pipe them. Because of slight pressure differences, it will always make it through one before it gets through the other.

Use a steam trap for each heat exchanger.

A steam trap in the area
has failed in the open position.

If a steam trap fails in the open position, it will pressurize the return and stop air from escaping. Check the traps and repair or replace them, if necessary.

Low- and high-pressure traps discharge into a
common line near the heat exchanger.

There will always be flash steam on the discharge side of an F&T trap or a bucket trap. How much flash steam you get depends on the pressure differential across the trap. The more differential pressure, the greater the amount of flash steam. Flash steam can

265

pressurize a return and keep both air and condensate from leaving a heat exchanger.

Returns under different pressures must discharge into a flash tank.

The steam pressure is too low.

As steam moves through pipes and valves, it loses pressure. In a commercial steam system, you depend on steam pressure to deliver a certain temperature to the heat exchangers. If the pressure is too low, you won't get the temperature you need. The heat exchanger may heat all the way across, but it won't heat to the temperature you need.

The same thing will happen if the pressure drop between the boiler and the heat exchanger changes. For instance, suppose someone changes a control valve, replacing a larger one with a smaller one. The pressure drop across the new control valve will be greater, so you'll wind up with less pressure (and temperature) at your heat exchanger.

Check the pressure and the pressure drop. Correct them as necessary.

THE BOILER SHUTS DOWN ON LOW WATER.

There's a feeder/cutoff combination on the boiler.

A steam boiler that's taking care of the space-heating needs of a building might have a feeder/cutoff combination. This device will feed water into the boiler as the water level drops, and then cut power to the burner should the level continue to drop.

The vertical difference in water level between the feed point and low-water cutoff point in a combination unit is too close for a commercial boiler. In a commercial system, some condensate may never return to the boiler. That means the feeder has to work

268

harder, supplying water more quickly than it would to a space-heating boiler. The low-water cutoff will trip the burner on repeated nuisance shut-downs if you use a combination feeder/cutoff on a commercial boiler.

Replace the combination control with a separate low-water cutoff and feeder.

The feed pump is cavitating.

If the steam traps have failed in the open position, the condensate might be too hot for the condensate- or boiler-feed pump to handle. The pump will cavitate and be unable to move the returning condensate back into the boiler. If the boiler doesn't have an automatic feeder, it will shut off on low water.

In commercial steam systems, high-pressure return lines sometimes flash their steam in the returns rather than in flash tanks. This high-temperature condensate will quickly cause a feed pump to cavitate. Find out what's making the condensate so hot and cure it.

Another option is to use a steam-powered return pump or an electrically operated high-temperature return pump.

THE BOILER LEAKS.

The boiler is taking on too much fresh water.

Fresh water carries oxygen, and when you boil that water, the oxygen comes out of solution and rusts the boiler. This usually happens right at the boiler's water line, and you might not notice it right away because the steam will go up the chimney. You can spot it if you flood the boiler, though.

If most of the condensate doesn't return to the boiler, you can treat the feed water with an oxygen-scavenging chemical. Another option is to feed the boiler with water that has passed through a deaerator or a water heater.

THE BOILER-FEED PUMP'S RECEIVER OVERFLOWS.

There's a leak in a heat exchanger's tube bundle.

If the heat exchanger's shell doesn't have a vacuum breaker, condensate won't drain freely. As steam enters the shell, it will meet the undrained condensate and create water hammer. The hammering usually takes place at the far end of the shell, opposite the water tappings. This often causes the tube bundle to spring a leak. Once the bundle leaks, water flows into the shell, passes through the steam trap and overflows the boiler-feed pump's receiver.

Replace the damaged tube bundle.

The boiler's pressure is greater
than the pump's pressure.

The boiler-feed pump's job is to put the returning condensate back into the boiler. To do this, the pump has to produce a pressure that's higher than the boiler's operating pressure. As a rule of thumb, if the boiler operates at 50 psi or less, the pump should discharge at the boiler's operating pressure plus 5 psi. For instance, if you have the boiler set to operate at 2 psi, you'd throttle the condensate pump to discharge at 7 psi. If the boiler operates above 50 psi, the pump should discharge at the boiler's operating pressure plus 10 psi. So if the boiler were in a dry cleaner's shop producing, say, 100 psi, the pump would have to discharge at 110 psi.

If the pump's pressure can't overcome the boiler's pressure, the pump can't return the condensate to the boiler. Lower the boiler

273

pressure (if that makes sense), or increase the head pressure of the condensate pump (by replacing it).

The pump is cavitating.

If the steam traps have failed in the open position, the condensate might be too hot for the boiler-feed pump to handle. The pump will cavitate and refuse to move the returning condensate back into the boiler. The condensate will overflow from the receiver.

In commercial steam systems, high-pressure return lines sometimes flash their steam in the returns rather than in flash tanks. This high-temperature condensate will quickly cause a feed pump to cavitate, and the receiver to overflow. Find out what's making the condensate so hot and cure it.

Another option is to use a steam-powered return pump or an electrically operated high-temperature return pump.

If the condensate is not excessively hot, you may be able to cool it to a point where the pump will stop cavitating. You can do this by running the returning condensate through a radiator before it enters the pump's receiver.

THERE'S NOT ENOUGH TEMPERATURE AT THE HEAT EXCHANGER.

The pressure is too low.

As steam moves through pipes and valves it loses pressure. In a commercial steam system, you depend on steam pressure to deliver a certain temperature to the heat exchanger. If the pressure is too low, you won't get the temperature you need. The heat exchanger may heat all the way across, but it won't heat to the fluid or the air to the temperature you need.

Raise the steam pressure, if that's feasible.

The pipes are too small.

The smaller the pipe, the greater the pressure drop. If the pipes between the boiler and the heat exchanger or process equipment are too small, you won't wind up with the pressure you need at the end of the line.

The same thing might happen if someone changes a control valve—replacing a larger one with a smaller one. The pressure drop across the new control valve will be greater, so you'll wind up with less pressure (and temperature) at your heat exchanger or process equipment.

Either increase the steam pressure, or reduce the piping pressure drop by increasing the size of the pipes. Don't oversize the control valve. It will wiredraw and fail. Size the control valve to the load.

The steam quality is poor.

If the near-boiler piping is wrong, or if the water is dirty, the steam will carry water with it as it leaves the boiler. The water will cause the steam to condense on its way to your heat exchanger or process equipment. You'll wind up with less pressure, and less temperature than you need.

Clean the boiler, and correct the near-boiler piping, if necessary.

WATER CARRIES OVER FROM THE BOILER TO YOUR HEAT EXCHANGER OR PROCESS EQUIPMENT.

A quick-opening valve opened while the boiler was under pressure.

When a quick-opening valve snaps into action, it drops the pressure inside the boiler. This instantly releases the heat energy contained in the water and increases the steaming rate dramatically. It's like popping the cap on a well-shaken bottle of beer.

Now, given that the pipe size remains a constant, the velocity

279

of steam will increase as you lower the steam pressure. That's because, at the lower pressure, the steam takes up more space. It has to move faster to get its increased volume through the pipe. Remember, the load (the firing rate) is also a constant. The higher-velocity steam will pull water out of the boiler and send it flying down the pipes. This is a common problem in bakeries where they use steam to put a gloss on bread while it's baking in the oven.

Use a slower-opening valve or size your supply pipes to accept the steam at the lower pressure and the higher velocity.

The steam quality is poor.

If the near-boiler piping is wrong, or if the water is dirty, the steam will carry water with it as it leaves the boiler. The water will cause the steam to condense on its way to your heat exchanger or process equipment. You'll wind up with less pressure, and less temperature than you need at the end, and a lot of unwanted water.

Clean the boiler, and correct the near-boiler piping, if necessary.

The supply lines aren't dripped properly.

In supply lines where the steam and condensate travel in the same direction, there should be a drip line every 150 feet. If the steam and the condensate flow in opposite directions you need a drip every 50 feet.

If you drip into a dry return that ends in a condensate- or boiler-feed pump, make sure you use steam traps. Size those traps based on the load and the pressure differential, not the line size.

THERE'S FLASH STEAM AT THE BOILER-FEED PUMP'S RECEIVER.

There's no flash tank.

If you have high-pressure steam, flash steam will leave the steam traps along with the condensate. The higher the pressure differential, the more flash steam you'll get. A flash tank removes the flash steam before it can reach the receiver. Always use a flash tank when you have high-pressure steam or high-pressure and low-pressure lines on the same system.

THE BOILER TAKES A LONG TIME TO PRODUCE PRESSURE.

The boiler is underfired.

If you're not firing hard enough to produce the steam load you need, it will take a long time to reach pressure. Figuring loads in a commercial steam system is usually more difficult than it is for space heating. If the load varies, or suddenly increases, your boiler may not be able to keep up with it.

Calculate your loads carefully and size your boiler to the right capacity.

COMMERCIAL

The boiler's taking on too much feed water.

If your process doesn't return any, or most, of the condensate, the boiler will be taking on plenty of feed water. It takes longer to bring city water up to steam temperature than it does to convert hot condensate back into steam. It might pay to preheat your feed water with a water heater. Using a preheater also cuts down on the oxygen that will enter your boiler.

There's scale in the boiler.

Process boilers that take on a lot of feed water need to be chemically treated to keep them from scaling. Scale comes mostly from calcium and magnesium, elements that are natural to fresh water. Scale formation lowers heat transfer and lengthens the time it takes to make steam. Scale also increases fuel usage.

The water quality isn't right.

Dissolved solids in the boiler water can create wet steam, which also adds to the time it takes to produce pressure. If the pH is wrong, the boiler will either foam or corrode. Too high a pH causes foaming; too low a pH can cause corrosion. If you're using boiler chemicals, make sure they're the right mix.

Treat the water only for the problem you're having, or the potential problem you might have if you're in an area with poor-quality water. Know what the treatment contains. Follow the directions. If you're not sure of what you're doing, get help from a professional water-treatment company.

THE PRESSURE-REDUCING VALVE FAILED.

Someone sized the valve to the line, not to the load.

If the pressure-reducing valve (PRV) is the same size as the line it serves, it's most likely the wrong size. Size the PRV for the load, not the line. If the valve is too large, it will hunt for the right reduced pressure. The valve disc will sit very close to the valve seat, and wiredraw erosion will cause the valve to fail.

Never size a PRV to the line size. If you're not sure what to do, ask for help from a PRV manufacturer.

The low points in the PRV station aren't trapped.

It's important to drip the low points around the pressure-reducing valve. If water accumulates, the steam will meet it and create water hammer, which can kill a PRV.

Size the steam traps to the load and the pressure differential, not the line size.

Water is collecting in the wye strainers.

There should always be a strainer before a PRV. The strainer's job is to keep system sediment out of the valve. Sediment not only clogs the valve, but driven at high velocity by the steam, it can erode the valve's internal parts. If water gathers in a strainer, the steam can pick it up and propel it at the valve at very high speed.

That's why it's best to install a wye strainer that's on the inlet side of a PRV on its side. Piped this way, water can't accumulate inside the strainer. And make sure someone is cleaning those strainers regularly.

In a two-stage PRV station, the valves are too close together.

A two-stage station takes steam pressure from a high point, to a medium point, and then to a low point. Between the two valves, the steam expands, increases its velocity and becomes very turbulent. Valve manufacturers recommend minimum distances between their valves. Check their specifications, and see if your valves are far enough apart.

The load varies too much.

If the PRV serves a system such as a space-heating system, the load will vary widely at different times of the year. Here, it's best to use two pressure-reducing valves in parallel instead of one. Set up this way, one valve will handle one-third of the total load, while the other valve takes care of two-thirds of the total load. During light loads, you can use the smaller valve. During heavier loads, use the larger valve, or both valves. If you use one large valve it will wire-draw during times of light load.

THERE'S A SCREECHING NOISE AT THE PRV STATION.

The line leaving the pressure-reducing valve is too small.

When you reduce the pressure of steam, it expands in volume. If the line on the discharge side of the PRV is too small, the expanded steam will increase its velocity and make a screeching noise. Increase the size of the pipe. If you're not sure what size to use, check with a PRV manufacturer.

THERE'S EXCESSIVE FLASH STEAM IN THE PRV STATION'S DRIP LINE.

There's an unprimed bucket trap.

Steam's pressure and temperature are tied together in a definite way. For instance, steam at 5 psi is 227 degrees, while steam at 125 psi is 353 degrees. When steam enters a PRV at 125 psi and leaves at 5 psi, there's a moment when the low-pressure steam still contains the heat of the steam at the higher pressure. We call this superheated steam. It doesn't take long for the superheat to scatter into the piping, the air in the room, and anything else it touches.

This is why you shouldn't use a bucket trap to drip the outlet side of a PRV. Bucket traps have a water prime. If superheat hits that water, it will boil it. Without the water prime, a bucket trap will blow steam into the return lines. Use an F&T trap to drip the outlet side of a PRV.

THERE'S WATER HAMMER IN THE MAINS.

The mains aren't properly dripped.

If the steam and the condensate flow in the same direction, you have to drip the mains at least every 150 feet. If the steam and the condensate flow in opposite directions, you have to drip the mains at least every 50 feet.

The traps are sized for the wrong differential.

Size the drip traps for the right load at the higher pressure differential they'll see during peak operation. This will cause them to be undersized when you're first starting the system because the pressure will be lower then. Get rid of the start-up condensate manually by using drain valves. We call this a supervised start-up.

If you want your start-up to be unsupervised, install low-pressure traps at a level a bit higher in the drip line than the high-pressure traps. On start-up, the high-pressure traps won't pass much condensate. The condensate will rise in the drip and spill from the low-pressure traps. When the pressure reaches its operating point, the low-pressure traps will lock-out, and the high-pressure traps will take over.

THERE'S WATER HAMMER IN THE RETURN LINES.

Low- and high-pressure traps discharge into a common line.

There will always be flash steam on the discharge side of an F&T trap or a bucket trap. How much flash steam you get depends on the pressure differential across the trap. The greater the pressure differential, the more flash steam you'll see. When you mix low- and high-pressure return lines without benefit of a flash tank, you'll get water hammer.

Use a flash tank.

The return lines aren't properly pitched.

Return lines, downstream of steam traps, should pitch continuously back to the boiler-feed pump's receiver. If the pitch is bad, condensate will lay in the lines. Any flash steam that comes from the traps will meet the undrained condensate and cause it to hammer.

Correct the pitch so the condensate can drain.

(Check, too, the Problems that plague
ALL STEAM SYSTEMS section
and the Problems that plague
TWO-PIPE STEAM SYSTEMS section.)